WINTER KEYS TO
WOODY PLANTS
of MAINE

Christopher S. Campbell
and
Fay Hyland
Botanists

Mary L. F. Campbell
Illustrator

University of Maine at Orono Press, Orono, Maine
1978

Library of Congress Cataloging in Publication Data

Campbell, Christopher S.
    Winter keys to woody plants of Maine.

    Bibliography: p.
    1. Woody plants — Maine — Identification. 2. Trees in winter — Identification. I. Hyland, Fay, — II. Campbell, Mary L. F., ill. III. Title.
QK484.M2C35   582′.15′09741   74-30438

Manufactured in the United States of America

Revised edition.

9 8 7 6 5 4 3 2

ISBN 0–89101–034–3

DEDICATION

It is with the utmost respect and admiration for the man that we dedicate this publication on Maine woody plants to the memory of the late Professor Merritt Lyndon Fernald (1873-1950). His exceptionally keen interest in plants was evident even as a child. At the age of seventeen he had published a list of plants of special interest in the vicinity of Orono, Maine, his birthplace. His study of plants soon expanded when excursions took him to more distant places, including Mt. Bigelow, Mt. Katahdin, Saint John and Aroostook valleys in Maine and thence into eastern Canada, where he noted many new species and range extensions. From this early interest in taxonomic botany in Maine, Fernald went on, by invitation, to Harvard University, where, in the period of 1891-1950 he became co-author (with Professor B. L. Robinson) of the seventh edition of Gray's Manual of Botany (1908), and finally, after forty-two years, as culmination of a life-long systematic study of plants, author of the eighth edition of the Manual in 1950. From 1935-1937 he was Curator, and from 1937-1947 Director of the Gray Herbarium. These achievements stand as a monument to his success as the leading authority on the flora of eastern North America. His unbounded enthusiasm and dedication of purpose will serve as a stimulus for all those who genuinely seek knowledge of our Northeastern flora.

ACKNOWLEDGMENTS

The authors wish to thank the following for assistance in collecting specimens for illustrations: Lesley M. Eastman for *Smilax rotundifolia* L., *Arceuthobium pusillum* Peck, *Sassafras albidum* (Nutt.) Nees, and *Rhododendron maximum* L. (also for finding *Chimaphila maculata* (L.) Pursh, new for the State, and relocating *Cornus florida* L.); Jonathan T. Frueh for *Salix alba* L.; Louis E. Hand for *Ceanothus americanus* L. and *Vaccinium caesariense* Mackenz.; Francis O. Holmes for *Salix nigra* Marsh.; Robert B. Livingston for *Betula caerulea-grandis* Blanch.; Charles D. Richards for *Empetrum nigrum* L.; Frederic L. Steele for *Salix arctophila* Cockerell; Henry K. Svenson for *Quercus* spp. and *Lycium chinense* Mill.

We also wish to thank the staff of the University of Maine Press and the L. H. Thompson Printing Company of Brewer for their fine efforts in the publication and Philip L. Campbell for typing the manuscript.

TABLE OF CONTENTS

Map of Maine and inch and metric scale on inside of back cover.

INTRODUCTION

This study includes the woody plants indigenous to Maine and those escaped from cultivation and apparently established within the State. It is intended for use between the end of the growing season and the resumption of growth the following spring. A woody plant is here considered a seed plant which has a persistent, ligneous, aerial stem which usually increases in length and diameter each year.

In certain genera the absence of diagnostic features present in the growing season makes determination uncertain or impossible. In *Crataegus*, no attempt is made to delimit species. Only a portion of the entities are readily distinguishable in *Amelanchier* and especially in *Rubus*. Also the treatment of *Lonicera*, *Vaccinium*, *Salix*, and *Rosa* is not wholly definitive; their species should be verified in the growing season. Hybridization occurs in these genera and may also be encountered in *Juniperus*, *Populus*, *Betula*, *Quercus*, and *Pyrus*. Many varieties and forms (abbreviated var. and f. respectively) are more or less discernible in the winter. Some are included in the keys, but most (those designated by an asterisk *) are given in the notes following the keys. These notes are listed alphabetically by genus.

Certain species which lie on the borderline between herbaceous and woody have not been included in this work. For example, *Veronica officinalis* L., a common plant of fields and dry open areas, is usually considered to be herbaceous despite the fact that it has persistent leafy stems. *Vinca minor* L. and *Thymus serpyllum* L. are both woody plants which have escaped from cultivation and established themselves locally. Descriptions of these species may be found in Fernald, Gray's manual of Botany, edition 8.

Before using the keys, see Pl. XXXVI which illustrates *Rhus radicans* L. and *R. vernix* L. both of which are POISONOUS TO TOUCH.

Careful observations in the field will facilitate use of the keys. One should note habit, habitat, location, and critical features such as vestiges and position of fruit and inflorescence, bark, and armature. A magnifying lens improves observations of small features such as bundle scars, vestiture, and bud scales. Characters in the keys are based upon healthy, typical individuals.

There are two sections in the keys. The first section is the key to genera and aberrant species (an aberrant species is defined as a species which is either the sole representative of a genus in Maine or which is so different from other members of the genus as to require separate treatment). After determining the genus of a plant in the first section, one may determine the species by turning to the second section which provides a key to subgeneric entities arranged alphabetically by genus. In cases where a species of a genus with more than one species is included in the key to genera and aberrant species, it is keyed again in the second section.

The keys are dichotomous. They consist of paired, equal, and opposing statements or leads both of which should be read carefully before choosing between the two and proceeding below the selected lead. If the correct choice of lead is not immediately clear, one should proceed under both leads until further choices make it clear which of the first two leads should have been taken. When the character or characters of a lead are inconstant or unclear for a genus or species, that genus or species is keyed under both leads. The characters making up a lead are arranged in descending order of importance. The first character should be given more weight than succeeding ones. The glossary, which is based upon usage in the keys, should be consulted if a term is not understood. The plates, which are all original drawings, should be used to confirm determinations arrived at through the keys.

Nomenclature follows Fernald, *Gray's Manual of Botany*, edition 8, except that all specific epithets are decapitalized. Latin names are used throughout the text and the plates. Common or colloquial names with their latin equivalents, and latin names with their common or colloquial equivalents are listed in the index; page and plate numbers are given only after the latin names. Knowing only the common name, one may find the plant in the text and plates by referring to the latin name equivalent provided after the common name in the index.

LIST OF PLATES

KEY TO GENERA AND ABERRANT SPECIES

1. Plants parasitic on branches of *Picea* spp. and rarely *Larix laricina* and *Pinus strobus*; dwarf, 0.5-2 cm. tall.
    Arceuthobium pusillum (Pl. LVIII).

1. Plants not parasitic (autotrophic) and more than 2 cm. tall.
    2. Leaves persistent (except in *Larix laricina,* see number 3 below) and acicular, scale-like, subulate, linear, or lorate; wood resinous; fruit a cone (Gymnospermae).
        3. Leaves deciduous; leaf scars densely clustered on prominent spur branches or remote on fast-growing twigs.
            Larix laricina (Pl. II).
        3. Leaves persistent; spur branches absent.
            4. Leaves borne in fascicles of 2, 3, or 5, surrounded at base by a chartaceous sheath (sheath caducous in *Pinus strobus*).
                Pinus (Pl. IV).
            4. Leaves borne singly; sheath absent.
                5. Leaves scale-like or subulate, opposite or in whorls; scale-like leaves often bearing a minute dorsal gland; bark fibrous and shreddy.
                    6. Twigs terete or 4-angled, not in flat horizontal sprays; cones fleshy and berry-like, their scales neither distinct nor separating at maturity; leaves dimorphic (scale-like on old growth and subulate on young) or all subulate and whorled; shrubs or small trees of mostly dry habitats.
                        Juniperus (Pl. V).
                    6. Twigs flattened, arranged in flat, horizontal sprays; cones composed of coriaceous or slightly woody scales which are distinct and separating at maturity; leaves all scale-like and imbricated; trees of mostly moist habitats.
                        7. Twigs strongly flattened, 2-4 mm. wide; cones ovoid-oblong with basally attached, imbricated, tan or brown scales; found throughout the state in neutral to alkaline soil, often in bogs and swamps.
                            Thuja occidentalis (Pl. II).
                        7. Twigs slightly flattened, 1-1.5 mm. wide; cones globose, with tack-shaped, peltate, bluish and glaucous scales; found only in Knox, Waldo, and York counties in acidic bogs and swamps.
                            Chamaecyparis thyoides (Pl. II).
                5. Leaves linear or lorate, alternate, nonglandular; bark scaly, smooth, or fissured and ridged.
                    8. Leaves linear, 3-or 4-angled in cross-section, rolling readily between thumb and fingers, bearing stomata on all surfaces, radiating in all directions from twigs or somewhat crowded on upper side of twigs.
                        Picea (Pl. III).
                    8. Leaves lorate, not rolling readily between thumb and fingers, bearing stomata below only, usually spreading in one plane and thus appearing 2-ranked.
                        9. Leaves green on both surfaces or reddish or brownish in exposed habitats, lacking conspicuous white stomatal bands below, the apex mucronate; low, straggling shrub rarely exceeding 2 m. in height.
                            Taxus canadensis (Pl.I).
                        9. Leaves dark green above, bearing 2 conspicuous white stomatal bands below, their apices obtuse or emarginate (leaves from upper crown of *Abies balsamea* often acuminate); trees.
                            10. Leaves sessile (leaf scars circular), leaving smooth branches after falling, 1-3.2 cm. long; cone scales and bracts deciduous from erect cone axis; bark of trunk thin and smooth, with raised resin blisters.
                                *Abies balsamea** (Pl. I).
                            10. Leaves minutely petioled, the persistent petioles leaving the branches rough after the leaves have fallen, 0.8-1.3 cm. long; cone scales persistent on pendent cone; bark of trunk thick, fissured and ridged, the bark scales purple beneath.
                                Tsuga canadensis (Pl. I).

5

* Denotes additional keys on page 19, under "Notes from genus key."

2. Leaves deciduous or persistent and broad and flat or, if resembling those of the Gymnospermae, stems short (less than 0.4 m. long) and mostly tufted and heath-like; wood not resinous; fruit not a cone (Angiospermae).

  11. Leaves persistent and living.

    12. Plants forming dense, smoothly rounded tussocks which obscure stems near center of tussock; leaves spatulate; confined to arctic-alpine regions.

Diapensia lapponica (Pl. LI).

    12. Plants consisting of a single stem, or more or less cespitose but not forming dense, smoothly rounded tussocks; leaves broadest at or below middle, or, if broadest above middle, obovate, not spatulate.

      13. Leaves opposite or whorled.

        14. Leaves subulate, very sharp-pointed; occasional escape.

Phlox subulata (Pl. LIII).

        14. Leaves blunt to acute, not very sharp-pointed.

          15. Leaves decurrent, scale-like, closely imbricated on lateral branches; occasional escape.

Calluna vulgaris (Pl. LII).

          15. Leaves petiolate or sessile, broad and flat or with more or less revolute margins.

            16. Leaves opposite.

              17. Leaves as broad as long.

                18. Leaves crenate, uniformly green, bearing scattered, light hairs; stem pubescent; fruit a glandular capsule borne in pairs on an erect peduncle.

Linnaea borealis var. *americana* (Pl. LIX).

                18. Leaves entire, more or less variegated with white areas, glabrous; stem glabrous; fruit a scarlet berry crowned by 2 persistent calyces.

Mitchella repens (Pl. LIX).

              17. Leaves at least twice as long as broad.

                19. Leaves revolute-margined, often glaucous below; plants low, less than 0.7 m. high.

                  20. Twigs prominently flattened, erect to ascending; leaves 0.7-3.5 cm. long; plant of boggy areas throughout; common.

Kalmia polifolia (Pl. L).

                  20. Twigs terete, frequently depressed or prostrate; leaves 0.3-0.8 cm. long; plant of arctic-alpine region of Mt. Katahdin.

Loiseleuria procumbens (Pl. LII).

                19. Leaves not revolute-margined, green below; plants larger, frequently exceeding 0.7 m. in height.

Kalmia (Pl. L).

            16. Leaves whorled

              21. Leaf margins strongly revolute and nearly meeting leaving a light-colored slit along the middle of the leaf below; leaves less than 1 cm. long; stems cespitose.

                22. Plants procumbent; flower buds axillary; leaves spreading-reflexed.

Empetrum (Pl. XXXV).

                22. Plants erect; flower buds terminal; leaves ascending.

Corema conradii (Pl. XXXV).

              21. Leaf margins not revolute; leaves longer than 2 cm.; stems single, not cespitose.

                23. Leaves serrate; plants low, less than 0.25 m. tall.

Chimaphila (Pl. XLVII).

                23. Leaves entire; plants exceeding 0.25 m. and up to 2.5 m. in height.

Kalmia (Pl. L).

  13. Leaves alternate.

24. Leaves trifoliolate (rarely 5 leaflets in *Rubus hispidus*).
  25. Stems long trailing, beset with numerous bristles; petioles bristly, subtended by a pair of linear stipules; leaflets obovate to suborbicular, irregularly crenate.

  Rubus hispidus (Pl. XXXIII).
  25. Stems short, usually less than 5 cm. tall, ascending from a creeping rhizome, unarmed; petioles without bristles and subtending stipules (old petioles frequently persistent); leaflets obovate, entire except for 3 (sometimes 5) apical teeth.

  Potentilla tridentata (Pl. XXVI).
24. Leaves simple.
  26. Leaves narrow, 4 or more times longer than broad.
    27. Leaves more than 2 cm. long, white-tomentose below; plants exceeding 1.5 dm. in height, of acidic bogs.

    Andromeda glaucophylla (Pl. XLVIII).
    27. Leaves less than 1 cm. long, not strongly whitened below; plants low, less than 1.5 dm. tall, of dry habitats.
      28. Leaves densely clustered or remote and appressed.

      Hudsonia (Pl. XXXV).
      28. Leaves uniformly spaced along branches and ascending to spreading.
        29. Leaves flat in cross-section.

        Phyllodoce caerulea (Pl. LII).
        29. Leaves terete or plano-convex in cross-section.
          30. Leaves linear-oblong, obtuse, their margins strongly revolute and nearly meeting making a light-colored slit along middle of leaf below.
            31. Plants procumbent; flower buds axillary; leaves spreading-reflexed.

            Empetrum (Pl. XXXV).
            31. Plants erect; flower buds terminal; leaves ascending.

            Corema conradii (Pl. XXXV).
          30. Leaves acicular, acute, their margins not evident.

          Cassiope hypnoides (Pl. LII).
  26. Leaves broader, less than 4 times as long as broad.
    32. Leaves toothed.
      33. Leaves marcescent, rugose, red, evenly crenate-serrate; terminal flower bud large; plants matted and trailing, confined to arctic-alpine region of Mt. Katahdin.

      Arctostaphylos alpina (Pl. LI).
      33. Leaves more fully persistent, neither rugose nor red, their margins evenly to irregularly toothed; plants ascending, of lower altitudes.
        34. Leaves crowded toward summit of stem; plants less than 3 dm. tall.
          35. Leaves yielding a wintergreen odor when crushed; fruit a red, baccate capsule borne on a short axillary peduncle.

          Gaultheria procumbens (Pl. LIII).
          35. Leaves without a wintergreen odor; fruit a dry capsule in terminal, umbel-like racemes.

          Chimaphila (Pl. XLVII).
        34. Leaves uniformly spaced along stem; plants exceeding 3 dm. in height.
          36. Leaves obovate, apically toothed, entire toward the base, not scurfy, uniform in size.
            37. Leaves, twigs, and buds bearing yellow resin dots; buds red; common, especially in coastal counties.

            Myrica pensylvanica (Pl. XIV).
            37. Leaves, twigs, and buds not yellow-dotted; buds dark; found only on Isle au Haut.

            Ilex glabra (Pl. XXXVIII).
          36. Leaves oval to lanceolate, entire to serrulate, scurfy, especially below, commonly decreasing in size toward summit of stem.

          Chamaedaphne calyculata* (Pl. LIV).

7

32. Leaves entire.
    38. Plants prostrate or trailing, less than 2 dm. tall.
        39. Leaves glabrous.
            40. Stems and leaves scurfy; leaves rugulose and aromatic; fruit a dry capsule; plant confined to arctic-alpine region of Mt. Katahdin

Rhododendron lapponicum (Pl. XLIX).

            40. Stems and leaves not scurfy; leaves neither prominently rugose nor aromatic; fruit baccate; plants not confined to arctic-alpine region.
                41. Leaves 1.5-2 cm. long, obovate to obovate-oblong; fruit a baccate drupe, subtended by 5 sepals, borne on a short pedicel; plant of dry areas.

Arctostaphylos uva-ursi var. *coactilis* (Pl. LI).

                41. Leaves less than 1.7 cm. long, triangular to oblong-elliptic (broadest at or below middle); fruit a berry, crowned by 4 sepals, borne on a long pedicel; plant of acidic bogs and moist areas, also barrens.

Vaccinium (Pl. LIV).

        39. Leaves pubescent or setulose, at least below.
            42. Leaves 2-8 cm. long, pubescent, especially on margin and midrib below; fruit a 5-locular capsule.

Epigaea repens var. *glabrifolia* (Pl. LIII).

            42. Leaves less than 1.8 cm. long, setulose below; fruit a berry.
                43. Leaves with coarse, light-colored setae, ovate, 0.5-1 cm. long; stems long-trailing, setulose; fruit a white berry.

Gaultheria hispidula (Pl. LIII).

                43. Leaves with minute, dark-colored setae below, obovate, 0.5-1.8 cm. long; stems depressed, glabrous; fruit a red berry.

Vaccinium vitis-idaea var. *minus* (Pl. LIV).

    38. Plants erect or arching, normally exceeding 2 dm. in height.
        44. Leaves 3-25 cm. long; medium to large shrubs of very local occurrence in dry or moist woods.
            45. Leaves 8-25 cm. long, oblong to oblong-obovate; twigs and underside of leaves pubescent; flower buds very stout.

Rhododendron maximum (Pl. XLIX).

            45. Leaves 3-10 cm. long, elliptical; plant glabrous; flower buds narrow.

Kalmia latifolia (Pl. L).

        44. Leaves less than 5 cm. long; small to medium shrubs of wide and frequent occurrence, especially in acidic bogs.
            46. Leaves scurfy, especially below, commonly uniformly decreasing in size toward the summit of stem; leaf margin not revolute, entire to serrulate; fruit in elongate racemes.

*Chamaedaphne calyculata** (Pl. LIV).

            46. Leaves not scurfy, but more or less pubescent below; leaf margin revolute, entire; fruit in umbelliform racemes.
                47. Leaves with long rusty (sometimes white) wool below; twigs densely villous; plant erect; capsule dehiscing from base.

Ledum groenlandicum (Pl. LI).

                47. Leaves whitened below with minute tomentum; twigs glabrous and glaucous; plant usually arching; capsule dehiscing from apex.

Andromeda glaucophylla (Pl. XLVIII).

11. Leaves deciduous or marcescent due to incomplete abscission in *Quercus, Fagus, Comptonia,* and less often in other genera.
    48. Leaf scars opposite or whorled.
        49. Stems climbing or twining.
            50. Climbing by means of persistent, twining petioles; twigs angled.

Clematis (Pl. VI).

            50. Twining or trailing; twigs terete.

Lonicera (Pl. LX).

        49. Stems erect.

51. Buds subopposite, distinctly paired but not directly opposite one another.
  52. Buds covered by 1 cap-like scale; plants unarmed; inner bark not conspicuously bitter-tasting or yellow; fruit not persistent.

  Salix purpurea (Pl. VIII).
  52. Buds covered by several dark, light-margined scales; twigs usually spinescent; inner bark bitter-tasting, bright yellow; fruit a frequently persistent, bitter, black drupe.

  Rhamnus cathartica (Pl. XLI).
51. Buds strictly opposite or whorled (occasionally subopposite on fast growing twigs of species with normally strictly opposite phyllotaxis).
  53. Buds and twigs densely covered with peltate scales; rare.

  Shepherdia canadensis (Pl. XLIV).
  53. Buds and twigs not peltate-scaly.
    54. Buds usually whorled, barely emergent from epidermis; fruit a globose head of achenes; shrub of wet areas.

    Cephalanthus occidentalis (Pl. LIX).
    54. Buds usually opposite, clearly emergent from epidermis; fruit not capitate; trees or shrubs of wet or dry areas.
      55. Pith hollow or excavated; escapes.
        56. Larger buds less than 1.5 mm. long, not superposed; bundle scar 1; twigs slender; fruit a commonly persistent white berry.

        Symphoricarpos albus var. *laevigatus* (Pl. LXII).
        56. Larger buds exceeding 1.5 mm. in length, often superposed; bundle scars 3; twigs moderate; fruit rarely persistent.

        Lonicera (Pl. LXI).
      55. Pith solid; natives or escapes.
        57. Bundle scars 3, separate (this lead includes some members of the genera *Lonicera* and *Cornus* in which the bundle scars are more or less obscure as a result of a persistent petiole base).
          58. Buds naked; buds and frequently twigs scurfy.

          Viburnum alnifolium (Pl. LXII).
          58. Buds covered by 1 or more scales.
            59. Bud scales 2, connate, appearing as 1; fruit a red drupe.

            Viburnum (Pl. LXIII).
            59. Bud scales 2 or more, distinct; fruit, if drupaceous, not red.
              60. Bud scales 2, valvate (in the terminal bud of some members of the genera *Viburnum* and *Cornus,* the bud scales may not completely cover the flower bud; see Pls. XLV, XLVI, and LXIII).
                61. Buds scurfy, linear.

                Viburnum (Pl. LXIII).
                61. Buds not scurfy, deltoid to ovoid-oblong.
                  62. Epidermis of branchlets and twigs cracking longitudinally; buds deltoid to ovoid; buds and twigs with spreading pubescence or gland-tipped hairs or both; low shrub rarely exceeding 1 m. in height.

                  Lonicera villosa (Pl. LX).
                  62. Epidermis not cracking; buds ovoid to ovoid-oblong; buds and twigs glabrous or with appressed to ascending pubescence; small trees or shrubs exceeding 1 m. in height.
                    63. 1 pair of interior, membranaceous, white scales prespent; petiole abscising at leaf scar; terminal bud scales meeting along their margins from base to apex; buds and twigs glabrous or white-puberulent; inflorescence spiciform or racemose; fruit a double samara.

                    Acer (Pl. XL).
                    63. Interior scales absent; petiole base frequently persistent; terminal bud scales frequently not meeting

along their margins around the flower bud; buds and twigs more or less dark pubescent; inflorescence cymose; fruit a drupe.

Cornus (Pl. XLVI).

60. Bud scales more than 2, imbricate.
    64. Twigs prominently lenticellate; terminal bud absent; leaf scars broad; bundle scars usually exceeding 3.

Sambucus (Pl. LXI).

    64. Twigs not prominently lenticellate; terminal bud present unless replaced by vestiges of inflorescence; leaf scars narrow; bundle scars rarely exceeding 3.
        65. Twigs usually glaucous; leaf scars connected by ridges which meet in a raised point; buds white-sericeous.

Acer negundo (Pl. XXXIX).

        65. Twigs not glaucous; leaf scars not connected by lines or connected by merely transverse lines; buds glabrous or dark-pubescent.
            66. Sap milky (as seen from sectioned bud scales); escape.

Acer platanoides (Pl. XXXIX).

            66. Sap watery; natives.
                67. Buds and twigs more or less reddish; collateral buds common on old growth; buds blunt to subacute.

Acer (Pl. XL).

                67. Buds and twigs tan, gray, purple or brown; collateral buds absent (superposed buds in *Lonicera canadensis*); buds acute.
                    68. Buds scales 4; inflorescence a terminal cyme.

Viburnum (Pl. LXII).

                    68. Bud scales more than 4; inflorescence an axillary peduncle bearing two partially fused berries or a terminal corymb or cyme.
                        69. Buds either divaricate or with loose scales; inflorescence an axillary peduncle bearing 2 berries (peduncle and less often berries more or less persistent).

Lonicera (Pl. LX).

                        69. Buds appressed and with tightly appressed scales; inflorescence a terminal corymb or cyme.
                            70. Twigs bearing decurrent ridges from nodes; fruit a 2-valved, beaked capsule borne usually in 3's in terminal cymes; low arching shrub usually less than 1 m. tall.

Diervilla lonicera (Pl. LIX).

                            70. Twigs without decurrent ridges; fruit a double samara borne in terminal corymbs; large forest tree.

Acer saccharum (Pl. XXXIX).

57. Bundle scars appearing as 1 or more than 3 and either separate or confluent (petiole base rarely persistent).
    71. Bud scales scurfy; bundle scars many in an elliptical or U-shaped aggregate; terminal bud present; fruit a samara; trees.

Fraxinus (Pl. LVII).

    71. Bud scales glabrous; bundle scars 7 or less; terminal bud absent; fruit a capsule or berry; shrubs.
        72. Twigs prominently lenticellate, weak; bundle scars 3 to 7, separate; fruit not persistent; inflorescence represented by a terminal peduncle; bruised bark malodorous; natives.

Sambucus (Pl. LXI).

        72. Twigs not prominently lenticellate, strong and rigid; bundle scar 1 (many small bundle scars confluent in a transverse line); fruit a commonly persistent capsule borne in panicles; bruised bark not malodorous; escape.

Syringa vulgaris (Pl. LVII).

48. Leaf scars alternate.
    73. Stems surrounded by loose, spongy tissue; buds divaricate, brown, barely emergent from spongy tissue; stem woody only at base, dying back to the spongy base; strictly aquatic, living portion frequently submerged with emergent marcescent stem.

Decodon verticillatus (Pl. XLIV).

73. Stems not surrounded by loose spongy tissue; buds clearly visible or sometimes submerged below level of epidermis or persistent petiole base and stipules; stem woody to apex; terrestrial to semi-aquatic, much of the living stem emergent if growing in water.

74. Stems climbing, twining, trailing, or prostrate.

75. Plants armed.

76. Plants arching or trailing; twigs mostly red.

77. Armature of paired spines at nodes; foliage rarely persistent; fruit a red hip borne in panicles; buds less than 4 mm. long; plants arching; escape.

Rosa multiflora (Pl. XXXI).

77. Armature of numerous internodal bristles and prickles; foliage usually marcescent to fully persistent; fruit an aggregate drupe, rarely persistent; buds exceeding 6 mm. in length; plants trailing; native.

Rubus hispidus (Pl. XXXIII).

76. Plants climbing or twining; twigs bright green, yellow, or tan-colored.

78. Armature consisting of stout longitudinally flattened spines; climbing by tendrils arising from persistent petiole base; buds hidden by petiole base; bundle scars 5-12 (evident only after removal of petiole base); twigs green, not ridged; vascular bundles scattered (make cross-section of stem).

Smilax rotundifolia (Pl. VI).

78. Armature consisting of spinescent branches; plants twining; buds exposed; bundle scar 1; twigs yellow or tan-colored, ridged; vascular bundles arranged in a ring.

Lycium chinense (Pl. LVIII).

75. Plants unarmed.

79. Climbing by tendrils or aerial rootlets; bundle scars several to many (not normally hidden by marcescent leaves of petiole bases).

80. Climbing by tendrils opposite leaf scars; buds covered by 2-3 scales, sessile; stipule scars long and narrow; twigs swollen and pith more compact at nodes.

81. Tendrils thickened at tips; pith greenish-white; epidermis lenticellate, not exfoliating after first year of growth.

Parthenocissus (Pl. XLII).

81. Tendrils not thickened at tips; pith brown; epidermis not lenticellate, exfoliating after the first year.

Vitis (Pl. XLIII).

80. Climbing by aerial rootlets arising from internodal areas; buds naked, often stalked; stipule scars absent; twigs not swollen and pith not more compact at nodes; POISONOUS TO TOUCH.

Rhus radicans (Pl. XXXVI).

79. Climbing, twining, trailing, or prostrate without specialized appendages; bundle scars 1-3 (obscured in *Arctostaphylos* and *Rubus* by marcescent leaves or persistent petiole bases).

82. Climbing or twining; leaves completely deciduous.

83. Bud scales distinct, sharply mucronate; twigs brown; native.

*Celastrus scandens** (Pl. XXXIX).

83. Bud scales indistinct, not mucronate; twigs pale or grayish; escapes.

84. Twigs prominently ridged; infrequent.

Lycium chinense (Pl. LVIII).

84. Twigs terete; common.

*Solanum dulcamara** (Pl. LVIII).

82. Trailing or prostrate; leaves stipules or petiole bases frequently persistent.

85. Twigs tipped by a large flower bud; distinctly woody perennial confined to arctic-alpine region of Mt. Katahdin (marcescent, red, rugose leaves commonly present).

Arctostaphylos alpina (Pl. LI).

85. Twigs dying or rooting at tip; barely woody biennial of low altitudes (marcescent stipules and persistent petiole base commonly present).

Rubus pubescens (Pl. XXXII).

74. Stems erect.
    86. Plants armed with thorns, spinescent branches, spines, prickles or bristles.
        87. Armature of thorns or spinescent branches.
            88. Armature of thorns in the axils of leaf scar; buds globose, obtuse.
                89. Shrub; twigs prominently ridged; bundle scar 1; buds dark brown, pubescent.

Lycium chinense (Pl. LVIII).

                89. Shrubs or small trees; twigs terete; bundle scars 3; buds reddish, glabrous.

Crataegus (Pl. XXVI).

            88. Armature of spinescent branches; buds ovoid, acute.

Prunus nigra (Pl. XXVII).

        87. Armature of spines, prickles, or bristles.
            90. Armature nodal, consisting of 1, 2, or 3 spines beside the leaf scar; internodal spines, prickles or bristles present in some.
                91. Armature of paired, nodal spines.
                    92. Buds submerged below rough leaf scar, more or less evident through a fringed crack.

Robinia (Pl. XXXIV).

                    92. Buds emergent.
                        93. Buds tomentose, indistinctly scaly, collateral; leaf scars broadly triangular; twigs pungently aromatic with citric acid odor; armature confined to paired nodal spines; rare escape.

Zanthoxylum americanum (Pl. XXXIV).

                        93. Buds glabrous, clearly scaly, borne singly; leaf scars very narrow; twigs not aromatic; armature of nodal spines and often of internodal spines, prickles, or bristles, especially on older growth; natives and escapes.

Rosa (Pls. XXX & XXXI).

                91. Nodal spines not regularly paired.
                    94. Leaf scars minute, borne on persistent leaf bases which are fascicled between simple or branched spines and bud; twigs sulcate; inner bark and wood bright yellow; epidermis not cracking; spines (modified leaves) strictly nodal; fruit a commonly persistent red berry; escapes.

Berberis (Pl. XXII).

                    94. Leaf scars large, not borne on persistent leaf bases and not fascicled; twigs not sulcate; inner bark and wood not bright yellow; epidermis tending to crack or shred; internodal spines often present; fruit not persistent; natives.

Ribes (Pls. XXII & XXIII).

        90. Armature internodal, not regularly consisting of 1-3 spines or prickles associated with nodes.
            95. Stems biennial, consisting of a marcescent floricane with more or less persistent vestiges of inflorescence and a living, arching or doming, cane-like primocane; petiole base commonly persistent.

Rubus (Pl. XXXII).

            95. Stems perennial; petiole bases not normally persistent.
                96. Leaf scars orbicular; buds submerged below crack in epidermis; twigs very bristly; occasional escape.

Robinia hispida (PL. XXXIV).

                96. Leaf scars narrow; bud completely emergent above leaf scar; twigs prickly or spiny; natives.
                  97. Bundle scars several to 12; leaf scars fringed with a palisade of densely packed prickles between leaf scar and bud; stems short-lived.

Aralia hispida (Pl. XLV).

                  97. Bundle scars 3; leaf scar not fringed (or if somewhat fringed with prickles, these loosely spreading and below leaf scar); stems persisting several years.
                    98. Buds covered by 5 or more scales; twigs yellowish or brownish,

decurrently ridged from the nodes; fruit not persistent.

Ribes (Pls. XXII & XXIII).

98. Buds covered by 3 or 4 scales; twigs reddish, not decurrently ridged; fruit a persistant red. hip.

Rosa (Pls. XXX & XXXI).

86. Plants unarmed.

99. Buds not visible, either submerged below leaf scar or hidden by persistent petiole base and stipules.

  100. Buds submerged below fringed crack in leaf scar; stipular spines more or less developed, especially on fast-growing twigs; fruit a legume; medium-sized tree often escaping and established near civilization.

Robinia pseudo-acacia (Pl. XXXIV).

  100. Buds hidden by persistent petiole base and stipules; plant unarmed; fruit a head of villous achenes surrounded by a persistent calyx; native shrub up to 1 m., of wet or dry, especially calcareous soils.

Potentilla fruticosa (Pl. XXVI).

99. Buds visible.

  101. Stems biennial, consisting of a marcescent floricane with more or less persistent vestiges of inflorescence and a living, arching or doming, cane-like primocane; petiole base commonly persistent.

Rubus (Pl. XXXII).

  101. Stems perennial; leaf abscission complete or leaves marcescent at some but not all nodes in *Quercus, Fagus, Comptonia*, and occasionally others.

    102. Leaf scars nearly encircling buds.

      103. Stipule scar a thin line encircling twig; buds glabrous; uncommon tree with mottled bark and fruit a globose multiple of achenes.

Platanus occidentalis (Pl. XXIV).

      103. Stipule scars absent; buds pubescent; shrubs with fruit drupaceous or absent.

        104. Twigs, branchlets, and main stems exceedingly flexible; bark leathery and tough; twigs conspicously constricted, joint-like between successive years of growth; buds scaly; sap not milky; plant of rich woods.

Dirca palustris (Pl. XLIV).

        104. Branchlets, twigs, and main stems stiff; bark not leathery; buds naked; sap milky; plants of open, sterile areas.

Rhus (Pl. XXXVII).

    102. Leaf scars extending less than three-quarters of the way around buds.

      105. Pith chambered or diaphragmed.

        106. Pith chambered, dark brown; leaf scars fringed along upper margin; bundle scars many, more or less compounded into three groups; buds tan-colored, often superposed.

Juglans cinerea (Pl. XIV).

        106. Pith diaphragmed, light-colored; leaf scars not fringed; bundle scars 3; buds dark, borne singly.

Nyssa sylvatica (Pl. XLVII).

      105. Pith homogeneous.

        107. Buds naked.

          108. Buds, at least the terminal, conspicuously scalpel-blade-shaped; flowers autumnal, following leaf abscission, with 4 lorate, yellow petals; fruit a 2-locular, 2-seeded, woody capsule.

Hamamelis virginiana (Pl. XXIV).

          108. Buds conical to ovoid; flowers absent; fruit a 3-valved capsule or a drupe.

            109. Bundle scar 1; twigs stellate pubescent; fruit a 3-valved capsule borne in erect, cylindrical panicles; local in southern Maine.

Clethra alnifolia (Pl. XLVIII).

            109. Bundle scars more than 1; twigs not stellate pubescent; fruit drupaceous.

13

110. Bundle scars 3; fruit in small, sessile umbels; escape.

Rhamnus frangula (Pl. XLI).

110. Bundle scars more than 3; fruit in panicles; natives; two of three species (those on Pl. XXXVI) POISONOUS TO TOUCH.

Rhus (Pls. XXXVI & XXXVII).

107. Buds covered by 1 or more scales.
   111. Buds covered by a single, cap-like scale.

Salix (Pls. VIII to XIII).

   111. Buds covered by 2 or more scales.
      112. Bundle scar 1 or appearing as 1.
         113. Twigs aromatic, yielding a fragrant odor when epidermis scraped; infrequent plants of southwestern Maine.
            114. Buds solitary, sessile; twigs bright green; large shrub or small tree with light-colored, flaky bark growing in dry places.

*Sassafras albidum** (Pl. XXIV).

            114. Buds often superposed and collateral, the floral buds stalked; twigs dark brown; shrub not exceeding 2.5 m. in height and growing in low moist areas.

Lindera benzoin (Pl. XXIV).

         113. Twigs not aromatic.
            115. Stipular vestiges or scars present beside leaf scars.
               116. Buds up to 7 mm. long; shrub of northern bogs.

Rhamnus alnifolia (Pl. XLI).

               116. Buds less than 3 mm. long; shrubs of dry or moist areas.
                  117. Low, less than 1 m. tall; stipules completely deciduous; barely woody shrub with paniculate inflorescence of persistent fruit bases; rare and local.

Ceanothus americanus (Pl. XLI).

                  117. Larger, up to 4 m. tall; stipular vestiges minute projections beside leaf scars; inflorescence a simple peduncle with usually 1 red, baccate drupe.

Ilex (Pl. XXXVIII).

            115. Stipular vestiges or scars absent.
               118. Inflorescence a long-persistent terminal panicle of aggregated follicles; leaf scar shriveled, the bundle scar separated from crescent-shaped lower portion of leaf scar.

Spiraea (Pl. XXXIII).

               118. Inflorescence not a terminal panicle of aggregated follicles; leaf scar not shriveled, the bundle scar not separated from leaf scar.
               119. Twigs prominently ridged; escapes.

Lycium chinense (Pl. LVIII).

               119. Twigs not prominently ridged; natives.
                  120. Terminal bud present.
                     121. Twigs stellate-pubescent; fruit a 3-valved capsule borne in erect, cylindrical panicles.

Clethra alnifolia (Pl. XLVIII).

                     121. Twigs either glabrous or with simple hairs; fruit a 5-valved capsule or not persistent.
                        122. Twigs and buds dark purple; bud scales 2-3; buds not conspicuously diminishing in size basipetally; fruit not persistent.

Nemopanthus mucronata (Pl. XXXVIII).

                        122. Twigs and buds pink to dark brown; bud scales 6 or more, at least in the larger buds toward apex of twig; buds conspicuously diminishing in size basipetally; fruit a commonly persistent 5-valved capsule.

Rhododendron (Pl. XLIX).

14

120. Terminal bud absent.
    123. Bud scales 2.
        124. Erect, 0.4-4 m. tall; fruit a persistent capsule borne in panicles.

            Lyonia ligustrina (Pl. XLVIII).

        124. Dwarf, depressed or ascending, less than 0.3 m. tall; fruit not persistent; inflorescence a simple axillary peduncle.

            Vaccinium cespitosum (Pl. LVI).

    123. Bud scales 3 or more.
        125. Buds obtuse; only 1 type of bud present; twigs brown; epidermis shreddy.

            Vaccinium uliginosum var. *alpinum* (Pl. LVI).

        125. Buds acute to acuminate; both vegetative and floral buds often present; twigs green, red, or black; epidermis not shreddy.
            126. Twigs papillose; bud scales of vegetative buds loose.

            Vaccinium (Pls. LV & LVI)

            126. Twigs smooth, not minutely roughened by pebbly projections; bud scales appressed.

            Gaylussacia (Pl. LV).

112. Bundle scars more than 1.
    127. Plants low, not exceeding 1 dm. in height above a horizontal rhizome; bud 1, terminal; stem covered by many approximate leaf scars.

            Aralia nudicaulis (Pl. XLV).

    127. Plants exceeding 1 dm.; buds more than 1; leaf scars, except on spur shoots, remote.
        128. Preformed catkins present.
            129. Stipule scars absent; buds and larger, apical catkins similar, their scales dark with a light margin.

            Myrica gale (Pl. XIV).

            129. Stipule scars present; buds and catkins dissimilar, their scales light-colored or, if dark, without a light margin.
                130. Two types of catkins present (large staminate and smaller pistillate); buds stalked.

            Alnus (Pl. XV).

            130. One type of catkin (staminate) present; buds sessile.
                131. Terminal bud present; phyllotaxis 1/3.

            Alnus (Pl. XV).

                131. Terminal bud absent; phyllotaxis 1/2 or 2/5.
                    132. Trees exceeding 5 m. in height.
                        133. Bud scales striate; bark gray with conspicuous, loose, vertical scales; wood exceedingly hard.

            *Ostrya virginiana** (Pl. XVIII).

                        133. Bud scales not striate; bark white, yellowish, black, or silvery gray, exfoliating horizontally or blocky, not with loose vertical scales.

            Betula (Pls. XVI & XVII).

                    132. Shrubs less than 5 m. tall.
                        134. Twigs aromatic, bearing yellow resin dots; linear, pinnatifid, marcescent leaves common; low (less than 1.5m. tall) shrub of dry, sterile, open areas.

            Comptonia peregrina (Pl. XIV).

                        134. Twigs not aromatic; resinous-dotted only in alpine *Betula glandulosa* (and then the dots not yellow); leaves rarely marcescent; plants not commonly of dry, sterile, open areas.
                        135. Catkins light tan-colored; buds with 4 or more scales; plants of dry to moist woods and thickets.

            Corylus (Pl. XVIII).

                        135. Catkins dark brown or greenish-yellow; buds with less

than 4 scales except on spur shoots; plants or alpine or paludal habitats.

Betula (Pls. XVI & XVII).

128. Preformed catkins absent.
    136. Terminal bud absent, the end bud pseudoterminal (except on spur shoots).
       137. Bud scales 4 or less (except on spur shoots).
          138. Bud scales deep red; fruit a globose, dry drupelet borne in cymes attached to a ligulate bract.

Tilia americana (Pl. XLIV).

          138. Bud scales dark brown, grayish, tan-colored, greenish or yellowish; fruit various but not borne in cymes attached to a bract.
             139. Buds covered by 2 pairs of equal scales, the inner pair densely grayish pubescent and as long as the bud, the outer pair darker and ⅓ to ⅔'s the length of the bud.

Corylus cornuta (Pl. XVIII).

             139. Bud scales not in equal pairs, color contrast not as above.
                140. Leaf scars semi-circular; fruit a bur or drupe, rarely persistent.
                   141. Pith stellate; twigs more or less fluted; bundle scars 3 but often compounded into many; rare tree of uplands.

Castanea dentata (Pl. XIX).

                   141. Pith terete; twigs terete; bundle scars 3, separate or confluent; shrub of cold bogs not exceeding 2 m. in height.

Rhamnus alnifolia (Pl. XLI).

                140. Leaf scars semi-ellipitical; fruit a nutlet borne in strobili.

Betula (Pls. XVI & XVII).

       137. Bud scales 5 or more.
          142. Buds 4-angled, more or less square in cross section; small tree of infrequent distribution with a fluted trunk covered by smooth blue-gray bark.

Carpinus caroliniana var. *virginiana* (Pl. XVIII).

          142. Buds not 4-angled, terete or laterally flattened; trunk and bark not as above.
             143. Stipule scars present; buds solitary, mostly distichous.
                144. Twigs with coarse, red, gland-tipped hairs (at least near buds); buds red, globose to short-ovoid, obtuse; shrub.

Corylus americana (Pl. XVIII).

                144. Twigs glabrous to pubescent but without coarse, red gland-tipped hairs; buds brown to yellowish-green, acute, ovoid; trees with scaly or ridged bark.
                   145. Buds vertically striate, yellowish-green, terete; bark consisting of freely peeling, grayish-brown, vertical scales; tree of rich uplands.

*Ostrya virginiana** (Pl. XVIII).

                   145. Buds not striate, brown, often laterally flattended; bark gray, corky-ridged; tree of bottomlands.

*Ulmus americana** (Pl. XIX).

             143. Stipule scars absent (obscure and mostly above leaf scar in *Prunus*); buds often collateral, not distichous.
                146. Buds less than 6 mm. long, acute, sessile; collateral buds equalling lateral bud; fruit rarely persistent; native or common escape.

Prunus (Pl. XXVII & XXVIII).

                146. Buds more than 6 mm., obtuse, often stalked with small collateral buds at the base; fruit an aggregate of follicles borne in large terminal panicles; occasional escape.

Sorbaria sorbifolia (Pl. XXXIII).

136. Terminal bud present.
    147. Leaf scars very narrow and elongate at right angles to the axis, several times longer than broad.

16

148. Terminal bud less than 4 mm. long; lateral buds frequently divergent; twigs frequently glaucous; fruit a commonly persistent hip.

Rosa (Pl. XXXI).

148. Terminal buds longer than 4 mm. long; lateral buds appressed to ascending; twigs not glaucous; fruit a berry or pome, not commonly persistent.

    149. Buds stalked, brown or pink, always uniformly colored.

Ribes (Pl. XXIII).

    149. Buds sessile, red, rufous, purple, or red and green.

        150. Second bud scale more than ½ length of bud; buds always uniformly colored.

Pyrus (Pls. XXVIII & XXIX).

        150. Second bud scale less than ½ length of bud; buds sometimes 2-colored; reddish and greenish.

Amelanchier (Pl. XXV).

147. Leaf scars broader, at most 3 times longer than broad.

    151. Pith stellate.

        152. Lowest bud scale of lateral buds centered over leaf scar; wood soft, diffuse-porous.

Populus (Pls. VII & VIII).

        152. Lowest bud scale of lateral buds not centered over leaf scar; wood hard, ring-porous.

            153. Buds clustered toward tip of twig; bud scales many; plants common.

Quercus (Pls. XX & XXI).

            153. Buds not clustered toward the tip of twig; bud scales few, plants infrequent.

                154. Terminal bud more than 10 mm. long; lateral buds divaricate; stipule scars absent; bud scales loose; leaf scar shield-shaped, bark shaggy.

Carya ovata (Pl. XIV).

                154. Terminal bud less than 7 mm. long; lateral buds ascending to spreading; bud scales tightly appressed; stipule scars present; leaf scars semi-circular; bark fissured and ridged.

Castanea dentata (Pl. XIX).

    151. Pith terete, or, if angled, without 5 points.

        155. Twigs aromatic, yielding a characteristic, fragrant odor when epidermis scraped.

            156. Buds solitary, sessile; twigs bright green; large shrub or small tree with light-colored flaky bark growing in dry places.

Sassafras albidum* (Pl. XXIV).

            156. Buds often superposed and collateral, the floral buds stalked; twigs dark brown; shrub not exceeding 2.5 m. in height and growing in low, moist places.

Lindera benzoin (Pl. XXIV).

        155. Twigs not aromatic, not yielding a characteristic fragrance, but may give off a fetid, or bitter-almond odor when epidermis scraped.

            157. Twigs and buds bearing yellow resin dots.

                158. Bud globose, obtuse, red.

Myrica pensylvanica (Pl. XIV).

                158. Buds ovoid, acute, brown.

Ribes americanum (Pl. XXIII).

            157. Twigs without yellow resin dots.

                159. Buds linear, yellowish-brown, divaricate; stipule scars encircling twig; fruit a triangular nut enclosed in a spiny husk; tree with smooth, gray bark.

Fagus grandifolia (Pl. XIX).

                159. Buds ovoid, obovoid, subglobose or oblong, appressed to slightly divergent; stipule scars, if present, separate, one on each side of the leaf scar.

                    160. Internodes very unequal, the nodes often clustered toward tip of twigs; shrub or small tree with horizontal branches.

Cornus alternifolia (Pl. XLV).

                    160. Internodes evenly spaced, the nodes not apically clustered (except on slow-growing shoots); branches ascending.

161. Buds stalked.
    162. Bundle scars 3; buds glabrous to sparingly pubescent.
        163. Stipule scars present; buds purple; phyllotaxis ⅓; pith triangular.

Alnus (Pl. XV).

        163. Stipule scars absent; buds brown or red; phyllotaxis not ⅓; pith terete.
            164. Pith brown; fruit an aggregate of follicles borne in large terminal panicles; buds obtuse, globose to ovoid; occasional escape.

Sorbaria sorbifolia (Pl. XXXIII).

            164. Pith white; vestiges of inflorescence an axillary rachis; buds acute, ovate-oblong; native.

Ribes (Pl. XXIII).

    162. Bundle scars 5 or more; buds densely pubescent; naked; POISONOUS TO TOUCH.

Rhus radicans (Pl. XXXVI).

161. Buds sessile.
    165. Epidermis exceedingly shreddy; fruit a capsule in umbelliform corymbs.

Physocarpus opulifolius (Pl. XXVI).

    165. Epidermis not shreddy; fruit not capsular and not in corymbs.
        166. Stipule scars present.
            167. Pith triangular; phyllotaxis ⅓; stipule scars wholly lateral to leaf scar; fruit a woody strobilus.

Alnus crispa (Pl. XV).

            167. Pith terete; phyllotaxis 2/5; stipule scars at least partly above leaf scar, fruit rarely persistent.

Prunus (Pls. XXVII & XXVIII).

        166. Stipule scars absent.
            168. Bundle scars 5 to many; two species (Pl. XXXVI) POISONOUS TO TOUCH.

Rhus (Pls. XXXVI & XXXVII).

            168. Bundle scars 3.
                169. Terminal bud and often lateral buds and twigs white tomentose; escape.

Pyrus malus (Pl. XXIX).

                169. Buds and twigs glabrous; natives.

Prunus (Pls. XXVII & XXVIII).

NOTES FROM GENUS KEY

(Listed alphabetically by genus)

Abies balsamea:
    a. Trees.
        b. Mature cones 3-8.5 cm. long, 2-3 cm. thick, their bracts shorter than scales; common.

A. balsamea.

        b. Mature cones 2-5.5 cm. long, 1.5-2 cm. thick, their bracts clearly exceeding the scales; infrequent.

A. b. var. phanerolepis.

    a. Prostrate shrub.

A. b. f. hudsonia.

Celastrus orbiculatus, which closely resembles *C. scandens*, is spreading from cultivation and becoming established.

Chamaedaphne calyculata:
    a. Leaves one-half as broad as long; sepals blunt.

C. c. var. latifolia.

    a. Leaves one-fourth to two-fifths as broad as long; sepals acute.

C. c. var. angustifolia.

Ostrya virginiana:
    a. Twigs nonglandular; frequent.

O. virginiana.

    a. Twigs bearing stalked glands; occasional.

O. v. f. glandulosa.

Sassafras albidum:
    a. Twigs glabrous.

S. albidum.

    a. Twigs pubescent.

S. a. var. molle.

Solanum dulcamara:
    a. Twigs glabrous to sparingly pubescent.

S. dulcamara.

    a. Twigs definitely pubescent.

S. d. var. villosissimum.

Ulmus americana: Several forms have been described. (*Ulmus rubra* is possibly indigenous to the State but is certainly extremely rare now if present at all.)

KEY TO SPECIES

ACER (Pls. XXXIX and XL).

1. Bud scales 2, valvate; body of fruit with a depression on one side; shrubs or small trees.
    2. Buds and twigs glabrous; older branches and stems green with vertical, white stripes; inflorescence racemose; wings of fruit spreading; depression in body of fruit smooth; large shrub or small tree.
        A. pensylvanicum.
    2. Buds and twigs white-puberulent (especially near the apex); older branches and stems light brown; inflorescence paniculate; wings of fruit more or less parallel; depression in body of fruit uneven; shrub.
        A. spicatum.
1. Bud scales more than 2, imbricate; body of fruit without a depression; trees.
    3. Buds and twigs reddish; collateral buds common on older growth; fruit and vestiges of inflorescence rarely present.
        4. Twigs yellowish below, curved, sublustrous; tree confined to borders of watercourses and bodies of water.
            A. saccharinum.
        4. Twigs uniformly red, straight, dull; abundant on a wide variety of sites.
            A. rubrum.
    3. Buds and twigs purplish, tan-colored, greenish or brownish; buds solitary; fruits or their vestiges commonly present (especially during mast years).
        5. Twigs glaucous, malodorous; lines connecting leaf scars meeting in a raised point; buds sericeous.
            A. negundo.
        5. Twigs not glaucous, not ill-smelling; lines connecting leaf scars transverse; buds glabrous or dark pubescent.
            6. Buds greenish or reddish-purple, obtuse, glabrous, short-oblong to subglobose; sap milky (as seen from sectioned bud scales); bark of mature trunk evenly furrowed; samaras up to 6 cm. long, the pairs forming an angle exceeding 80°; escape.
                A. platanoides.
            6. Buds dark brown, acute, often pubescent, ovoid to fusiform; sap watery; bark of mature trunk irregularly ridged, scaly; samaras up to 4 cm. long, the pairs forming a "u"; native.
                A. saccharum.

ALNUS (Pl. XV).

1. Buds sessile, glutinous; preformed staminate catkins only present; fruiting strobili on long slender pedicels; nutlets winged.
    2. Twigs glabrous; confined to arctic-alpine regions.
        A. crispa.
    2. Twigs puberulent, at least toward apex; common, arctic-alpine region and throughout the state.
        A. c. var. mollis.
1. Buds stalked, scurfy; preformed staminate and pistillate catkins present; fruiting strobili sessile or short-pedicelled; nutlets wingless.
    3. Main stem with coarse, white, horizontal lenticels; abundant throughout.
        A. rugosa.
    3. Main stem not prominently lenticellate; occasional in southwestern portion of state, infrequent northward.
        A. serrulata.

AMELANCHIER (Pl. XXV).

1. Leaves imbricate in bud.
    A. bartramiana.

1. Leaves conduplicate in bud.
    2. Plants stoloniferous.
        A. stolonifera.
    2. Plants solitary or colonial, not stoloniferous.
        3. Buds dark purple, northern.
            A. gaspensis.

3. Buds reddish, greenish, or yellowish.
    4. Twigs deep reddish-purple.

A. sanguinea.

    4. Twigs gray to reddish-brown.

A. laevis, A. arborea,
A. wiegandii, A. canadensis,
and A. intermedia.

(*A. arborea* is an infrequent plant of rich, neutral to alkaline soils; of the remaining oxylophytes, *A. laevis* is by far the most common.)

ARALIA (Pl. XLV).

1. Unarmed; stems low, less than 1.5 dm. tall, arising from a horizontal rhizome, bearing 1 terminal bud and many approximate leaf scars.

A. nudicaulis.

1. Armed with many bristles; stems up to 1 m., the tips marcescent, bearing several remote buds.

A. hispida.

ARCTOSTAPHYLOS (Pl. LI).

1. Leaves marcescent, rugose, regularly crenate-serrate; drupe black; confined to arctic-alpine region of Mt. Katahdin.

A. alpina.

1. Leaves persistent, plane, entire; drupe red; common plant of dry sterile areas of low elevations.

A. uva-ursi var. *coactilis.*

BERBERIS (Pl. XXII).

1. Twigs brown; spines mostly simple, occasionally with weak basal branches; fruit solitary or in small umbels; low, less than 1.5 m. tall; occasional escape.

B. thunbergii.

1. Twigs gray; spines frequently with 2 basal branches at base; fruit in racemes; up to 3 m. tall; common escape.

B. vulgaris.

BETULA (Pls. XVI & XVII).

1. Twigs emitting a wintergreen odor when epidermis scraped; large trees with dark brown, yellowish or gray bark.
    2. Twigs dark brown, glabrous; fruiting strobili short-cylindric, their bracts glabrous; bark of trunk dark brown, platy; occasional forest tree of southwestern portion of State.

B. lenta.

    2. Twigs usually tan-colored or light brown, more or less pubescent; fruiting strobili ovoid to subglobose, their bracts more or less pubescent; bark of trunk yellowish and exfoliating in papery horizontal strips, gray and platy in age; common forest tree throughout the State.

B. lutea*.

1. Twigs without a wintergreen odor; shrubs or trees with whitish or brown bark.
    3. Buds short-oblong to deltoid-ovoid, less than 5 mm. long, their scales uniformly dark; bark dark brown; shrubs; preformed staminate catkins oblong, less than 1.5 cm. long; fruiting strobili erect, less than 2 cm. long; plants confined to cold, northern bogs and the arctic-alpine region of Mt. Katahdin.
        4. Twigs either densely pubescent or coarsely warty-glandular; wing of nutlet narrower than to just as broad as body.
            5. Twigs densely pubescent; plant up to 4 m. tall, of cold, northern bogs.

B. pumila.

            5. Twigs essentially glabrous and conspicuously warty-glandular; plant up to 1 m. tall of arctic-alpine region of Mt. Katahdin.

B. glandulosa.

        4. Twigs glabrous and sparingly or not at all warty-glandular; wing of nutlet broader than body; plant up to 2 m. tall, confined to arctic-alpine region of Mr. Katahdin.

B. minor.

21

* Denotes additional keys on pages 34 and 35, under "Notes from species key."

3. Buds ovoid to fusiform, 3-9 mm. long, their scales often partially green or yellow; bark white (brown on trunks up to several years and in two varieties of *B. papyrifera;* trees (shrubs in exposed habitats); preformed staminate catkins linear, generally exceeding 3 cm. in length; fruiting strobili pendent, generally exceeding 2 cm. in length; plants of wide distribution (*B. papyrifera* the only one found in arctic-alpine region of Mt. Katahdin).

    6. Twigs conspicuously warty-glandular, thin, less than 2 mm. in diameter; buds small, 3-6 mm. long; preformed staminate catkins erect, usually solitary; bracts of fruiting strobili horizontally spreading, pubescent on back; small tree with white, non-exfoliating bark.

        B. populifolia.

    6. Twigs only slightly or not at all warty-glandular, up to 3.5 mm. in diameter; buds generally exceeding 5 mm. in length, preformed staminate catkins ascending to spreading, usually 2 or more on a twig; bracts of fruiting strobili ascending, glabrous; small to large trees with white, exfoliating bark (brown in varieties of *B. papyrifera*).

       7. Twigs glabrous; rare.

        B. caerulea-grandis.

       7. Twigs more or less pubescent; common.

        *B. papyrifera.**

CHIMAPHILA (Pl. XLVII).

1. Leaves variegated with white; extremely rare.

        C. maculata.

1. Leaves not variegated; common.

        C. umbellata var. *cisatlantica.*

CLEMATIS (Pl. VI).

1. Twigs dark, purplish; fruit absent; infrequent calciphyte of mostly rocky uplands.

        C. verticillaris

1. Twigs light yellowish-brown; fruit a cluster of long-villous achenes; common plant of acidic soils.

        C. virginiana.

CORNUS (Pls. XLV & XLVI).

1. Buds alternate, crowded towards tips of twigs; internodes very unequal.

        C. alternifolia.

1. Buds opposite, not crowded toward tips of twigs; internodes more or less equal.

    2. Lateral buds hidden; terminal flower bud globose or discoid; twigs often glaucous; small, rare tree with blocky bark.

        C. florida.

    2. Lateral buds evident; terminal flower bud ovoid; twigs not glaucous; infrequent to abundant shrubs.

      3. Pith brown.

        4. Twigs light brown, lenticellate; infrequent; cymes elongate.

        C. racemosa.

        4. Twigs dark purple, without prominent lenticels; common; cymes broad.

        C. amomum and *C. obliqua.*

      3. Pith white.

        5. Twigs prominently streaked with purple.

        C. rugosa.

        5. Twigs not prominently streaked.

         6. Twigs light brown; cymes elongate; infrequent.

        C. racemosa.

         6. Twigs bright red; cymes broad; abundant.

        C. stolonifera.

CORYLUS (Pl. XVIII).

1. Twigs with coarse, red, gland-tipped hairs (at least in protected areas near buds); buds with more than 4 uniformly reddish scales; preformed staminate catkins stalked; not extending north of latitude 45.

        C. americana.

1. Twigs without coarse, red, gland-tipped hairs; buds covered by 2 pairs of equal scales: 2 light-colored ones which are the full length of the bud and 2 darker ones which cover the lower ⅓ to ⅔'s of the bud; preformed staminate catkins sessile; throughout State.

C. cornuta.

EMPETRUM (Pl. XXXV).
1. Twigs glabrous; leaves spreading-reflexed.

E. nigrum.

1. Twigs more or less tomentose; leaves spreading-ascending.

E. atropurpureum.

FRAXINUS (Pl. LVII).
1. Lateral buds globose, the first pair not adjacent to terminal bud; inner layer of epidermis white or tan-colored; wing completely surrounding seed body of samara; small tree confined to bogs or wet areas; bark of trunk irregularly scaly or corky.

F. nigra.

1. Lateral buds laterally compressed, the first pair adjacent to terminal bud; inner layer of epidermis purple or cinnamon-colored; wing not completely surrounding seed body of samara; medium to large trees of uplands or margins of watercourses or bodies of water; bark of trunk with regularly anastomosing, non-corky ridges.
   2. Terminal bud dome-shaped; leaf scars deeply notched at apex; twigs glabrous, purple, especially when growing in the open; inner layer of epidermis purple; uplands.

F. americana.

   2. Terminal bud broadly conical; leaf scars truncate or more or less notched at apex; twigs pubescent to glabrous, gray; inner layer of epidermis cinnamon-colored; margins of watercourses or bodies of water.

F. pennsylvanica*.

GAULTHERIA (Pl. LIII).

1. Stems ascending; leaves clustered toward tip of stem, 1.5-5 cm. long, glabrous, serrate; fruit red.

G. procumbens.

1. Stems trailing; leaves uniformly spaced, 0.5-1 cm. long, setulose below, entire; fruit white.

G. hispidula.

GAYLUSSACIA (Pl. LV).

1. Low, less than 6 dm. high; bracts of inflorescence persistent; local, mostly confined to sandy swamps near coast.

G. dumosa var. *bigeloviana.*

1. Larger, up to 1.5 m. tall; bracts of inflorescence deciduous; common in wet or dry areas.

G. baccata.

HUDSONIA (Pl. XXXV).

1. Leaves less than 2 mm. long, appressed; plant hoary; on sea beaches, and inland sand plains.

H. tomentosa.*

1. Leaves more than 2.5 mm. long, ascending-divergent; plant villous; on rocks of coastal hills and mountains.

H. ericoides.

ILEX (Pl. XXXVIII).

1. Leaves persistent; drupe black; known only from Isle au Haut.

I. glabra.

1. Leaves deciduous; drupe red.
   2. Buds globose, not laterally compressed; abundant throughout.

I. verticillata.*

   2. Bud laterally compressed; local.

I. laevigata.

JUNIPERUS (Pl. V).

1. Leaves all subulate, in whorls of 3 (sometimes opposite;, eglandular, jointed at the base, bearing a broad white band along midrib above; fruit with conspicuous triangular scar at apex.

2. Arborescent; leaves wide-spreading; rare.

J. communis.

2. Shrubby; leaves spreading to subappressed; common to local.
   3. Decumbent, stems usually ascending at tips, forming large mats; leaves 8-18 mm. long, straight, sharp-pointed, spreading or ascending; common except in Northern Aroostook County.

J. c. var. depressa.

   3. Depressed and trailing; leaves 6-9 mm. long, curved, short-pointed, sub-appressed; local in exposed situations along seacoast and in mountains.

J. c. var. saxatilis.

1. Leaves dimorphic: mostly scale-like, opposite, appressed, imbricated, and bearing a minute dorsal gland or, or on young and vigorous growth, subulate, whorled, and eglandular; fruit without conspicuous apical triangle.
   4. Low creeping shrub with long, trailing branches bearing numerous short lateral branches; fruit with a few spiny projections near the tip, borne on recurved peduncles; local on sandy or rocky banks along coast.

J. horizontalis.

   4. Erect shrub or small tree with ascending or spreading branches forming a narrow crown; fruit nearly smooth, borne on straightish, erect peduncles; frequent in southwestern Maine.

J. virginiana var. *crebra.*

KALMIA (Pl. L).

1. Twigs prominently flattened; leaves opposite, glaucous below, their margins revolute; confined to bogs and other wet areas.

K. polifolia.

1. Twigs terete; leaves whorled, alternate, or uncommonly opposite, green below, their margins not revolute; found in wet or dry areas.
   2. Leaves whorled, occasionally opposite; corymbs axillary; slender, abundant shrub.

K. angustifolia.

   2. Leaves usually alternate, sometimes opposite or whorled; corymbs terminal; coarse, local shrub.

K. latifolia.

LONICERA (Pls. LX & LXI)

1. Trailing or climbing.

L. dioica and *sempervirens.*

1. Erect.
   2. Pith hollow; escapes.
      3. Buds and twigs glabrous.

L. tatarica.

      3. Buds or twigs or both pubescent.
         4. Buds fusiform, pubescent.

L. xylosteum.

         4. Buds conical, glabrescent.

L. morrowi.

   2. Pith solid; natives.
      5. Bud scales 2; twigs glabrous to pubescent, brown.

L. villosa.*

      5. Bud scales more than 2; twigs glabrous, gray or purplish.
         6. Buds divaricate, their scales obtuse, scarious-margined; common shrub of woodlands throughout.

L. canadensis.

         6. Buds appressed, their scales acute, not scarious-margined; occasional shrub of calcareous bogs of northern portion of State.

L. oblongifolia.

   NOTE: X *Lonicera bella*, a hybrid of *L. tatatica* and *L. morrowi*, is intermediate between these two and may be infrequently encountered.

MYRICA (Pl. XIV).

1. Buds red, globose, obtuse; fruits encrusted with bluish-white wax, unwinged; preformed catkins absent; dry places, chiefly coastal.

M. pensylvanica.

1. Buds dark brown, ovoid, acute; fruits not waxy, two-winged; preformed staminate catkins present; similar to but larger than vegetative or mixed buds; moist to wet areas throughout.

M. gale.

PARTHENOCISSUS (Pl. XLII).

1. Tendrils tipped by prominent suction discs.

P. quinquefolia.

1. Tendril tips only moderately flattened and flaring.

P. inserta.

PICEA (Pl. III).

1. Twigs glabrous and glaucous; cones nearly cylindrical, their scales flexible, tan-colored, entire, and generally truncate or slightly emarginate at apex.

P. glauca.

1. Twigs pubescent and not glaucous; cones ovoid to ovoid-oblong, their scales stiff, reddish- or purplish-brown, often erose, and rounded at apex.
   2. Leaves grayish-green, glaucous, dull, mostly blunt and projecting radially from twigs; twigs cinnamon-brown; cones stubby and ovoid, broad funnel-form at base, persisting on tree for many years; cone scales erose, purplish-brown, becoming indistinct near peduncle; outline of tree columnar or slenderly pyramidal; mostly confined to bogs.

P. mariana.

   2. Leaves yellow-green, not glaucous, lustrous, mostly acute, curved and incurved toward twig; twigs orange- or straw-yellow; cones ovoid-oblong, rounded at base, usually deciduous by spring following maturity; cone scales entire or denticulate, reddish-brown, distinct near peduncle; outline of tree pyramidal; shallow soils and rocky upland woods.

P. rubens.

PINUS (Pl. IV).

1. Leaves 5 in a fascicle; cones 10-20 cm. long; umbo terminal.

P. strobus.

1. Leaves less than 5 in a fascile; cones less than 10 cm. long; umbo dorsal.
   2. Leaves 3 (rarely 4) in a fascicle; cone scales armed with conspicuous, sharp, slender, broad-based prickles.

*P. rigida.**

   2. Leaves 2 in a fascicle; cone scales unarmed or with minute prickles.
      3. Leaves 12-17 cm. long; cones symmetrical, usually falling within a year of maturity and leaving a few basal scales on branch; cone scales unarmed.

P. resinosa.

      3. Leaves 2-4 cm. long; cones asymmetrical at base, persisting on tree for many years and not leaving scales on branches after falling; cone scales armed with minute, deciduous prickles.

P. banksiana.

POPULUS (Pls. VII & VIII).

1. Buds stout, up to 2.5 cm. long, resinous, fragrant.
   2. Twigs glabrous; common, especially northward.

P. balsamifera.

   2. Twigs with some long spreading hairs; infrequent and local.

X *P. gileadensis.*

1. Buds smaller, less than 1 cm. long, dry to scarcely resinous, not fragrant.
   3. Buds and twigs pubescent or tomentose.
      4. Buds and twigs finely pubescent; buds divergent; abundant throughout.

P. grandidentata.

      4. Buds and twigs hoary-tomentose; buds appressed to ascending; occasional escape.

P. alba.

   3. Buds and twigs glabrous.

5. Buds dark brown; leaf scars lunate; branches spreading to ascending; abundant throughout.

P. tremuloides*.

5. Buds yellowish-brown; leaf scars triangular to orbicular; branches fastigiate; infrequent escape.

P. nigra.

POTENTILLA (Pl. XXVI).

1. Leaves persistent, trifoliolate; buds visible; low, stems less than 1 dm. tall; oxylophyte.

P. tridentata*.

1. Leaves deciduous; buds hidden by persistent petiole base and stipules; shrub up to 1.5 m. tall; calciphyte.

P. fruticosa.

PRUNUS (Pls. XXVII & XXVIII).

1. Terminal bud absent.
   2. Twigs pubescent, unarmed; shrub of sandy soil near coast.

P. maritima.

   2. Twigs glabrous, frequently spinescent; large shrub or small tree of the interior.

P. nigra.

1. Terminal bud present.
   3. Buds less than 4 mm. long, blunt to subacute, uniformly reddish-brown, often clustered toward tip of twig; collateral buds present; twigs vinaceous; bitter-almond odor of bruised or scraped twigs not prominent.
      4. Low, less than 1 m. high (collateral buds present, even on low stems).
         5. Depressed or prostrate; confined to gravelly or sandy river-beaches.

P. depressa.

         5. Erect to ascending; sandy, open soil generally distant from rivers.

P. susquehanae.

      4. Large shrub or small tree; bark with orange lenticels.

P. pensylvanica.

   3. Buds of healthy, open-growing twigs exceeding 4 mm. in length, acute, their scales often with more than 1 color or shade, uniformly spaced along twig, solitary; bitter-almond odor of bruised or scraped twigs prominent.
      6. Buds laterally compressed, less than 6 mm. long, triangular-ovoid, their scales reddish-brown and greenish-yellow; tree, usually growing singly.

P. serotina.

      6. Buds terete, fusiform, up to 9 mm. long, their scales with a dark brown base and tan-colored toward apex; shrub or small tree, usually growing in clumps.

P. virginiana.

PYRUS (Pls. XXVIII & XXIX).

1. Buds conical to short-oblong, at least the terminal densely tomentose; tree with blocky bark.

P. malus.

1. Buds ovoid to oblong, glabrous to pubescent but not densely so, shrubs or small trees with smooth bark.
   2. Buds stout, exceeding 4 mm. in diameter at base and usually more than 9 mm. in length; bundle scars 5; inflorescence compound.
      3. Buds gummy, the outer scales glabrous to sparingly pubescent with dark hairs; twigs and vestiges of inflorescence glabrous; natives.

P. decora and americana.

      3. Buds scarcely gummy, the outer scales white pubescent; twigs and vestiges of inflorescence more or less villous; escape.

P. aucuparia.

   2. Buds moderate, less than 4 mm. in diameter at base and usually less than 9 mm. in length; bundle scars mostly 3; inflorescence simple.
      4. Buds dark purple, up to 9 mm. long, large shrub or small tree; local.

P. floribunda X P. aucuparia.

      4. Buds red, less than 7 mm. long; common shrubs.
         5. Twigs pubescent.

P. floribunda.

5. Twigs glabrous.

P. melanocarpa.

QUERCUS (Pls. XX & XXI).

1. Twigs and buds yellowish, tan-colored, gray or reddish-brown to purple; buds blunt to acute; acorns maturing in 1 year, first-year acorns absent; marcescent leaves with blunt lobes or teeth, lacking bristles; bark light grayish and flaky (brown to nearly black and furrowed in *Q. prinus*).

subgenus *Leucobalanus.*

    2. Twigs gray to purple; buds reddish-brown; common southward.

Q. alba.

    2. Twigs yellowish to tan-colored, buds yellowish to light reddish-brown; infrequent or local.

        3. Buds blunt to subacute; linear stipular vestiges persistent among terminal bud cluster; older branches either with corky or exfoliating bark; bark of trunk grayish.

            4. Branches with corky bark; twigs more or less pubescent.

Q. macrocarpa.

            4. Branches with exfoliating bark; twigs glabrous.

Q. bicolor.

        3. Buds acute; stipular vestiges absent; older branches smooth-barked to somewhat furrowed, without corky or exfoliating bark; bark of trunk brown to nearly black, deeply furrowed.

Q. prinus.

1. Twigs and buds dark brown; buds acute (blunt only in shrubby *Q. ilicifolia*); acorns maturing in 2 years, partly developed first-year acorns present in mature individuals; marcescent leaves with bristle-tipped lobes; bark dark, often furrowed in age.

subgenus *Erythrobalanus.*

    5. Buds blunt, the larger less than 4 mm. long; twigs pubescent; leaves irregularly lobed, the lobes triangular to ovate; shrub or small tree of dry, sterile sites.

Q. ilicifolia.

    5. Buds acute, the larger exceeding 4 mm. in length; twigs glabrous; leaves regularly lobed, the lobes oblong; trees.

        6. Bud prominently 5-angled and densely tan-tomentose, up to 12 mm. long; inner bark orange-colored.

Q. velutina.

        6. Buds terete to slightly angled, glabrous to sparingly pubescent; less than 10 mm. long; inner bark not orange-colored.

            7. Larger buds exceeding 1 cm. in length, glabrous to uniformly pubescent, conical, rather sharp-pointed; leaves with "U"-shaped sinuses; inner bark of trunk whitish; abundant, the most common oak in the State.

Q. rubra.*

            7. Larger buds less than 7 mm. in length, pubescent in the upper half, ovoid, blunt-pointed; leaves with "C"-shaped sinuses; inner bark of trunk yellowish; rare.

Q. coccinea.

RHAMNUS (Pl. XLI).

1. Buds subopposite, acute, their scales dark with a light-margin; twigs usually ending in a spine.

R. cathartica.

1. Buds alternate, obtuse to subacute, naked and villous or covered by uniformly dark scales; plants unarmed.

    2. Buds naked, villous, tan or brown in color; drupe commonly persistent; shrub or small tree introduced and frequently spreading in fields and thickets.

R. frangula.

    2. Buds covered by dark, glabrous scales; fruit rarely persisting; native shrub up to 1 m. tall, mostly of bogs or grassy swales.

R. alnifolia.

RHODODENDRON (Pl. XLIX).

1. Leaves persistent.

    2. Dwarf; leaves 0.5-2 cm. long, aromatic, rugose and scurfy; confined to arctic-alpine region of Mt. Katahdin.

R. lapponicum.

    2. Large shrub; leaves 8-25 cm. long, neither aromatic, rugose, not scurfy; local in damp, deep woods.

R. maximum.

1. Leaves deciduous.
   3. Twigs glabrous to soft pubescent; common.

R. canadense.

   3. Twigs strigose to hirsute; rare.

R. viscosum.

RHUS (Pls. XXXVI & XXXVII).

1. Leaf scars nearly encircling bud.
   2. Twigs and drupes densely villous; twigs terete, not glaucous.

R. typhina.

   2. Twigs glabrous, more or less 3-angled and glaucous; drupes with short, appressed hairs.

R. glabra*.

1. Leaf scars less than half encircling bud.
   3. Twigs densely pubescent; fruit a red, pubescent drupe in terminal panicles; local.

R. copallina var. *latifolia.*

   3. Twigs glabrous to sparingly pubescent; fruit a greenish- or brownish-white, baccate drupe in axillary panicles; POISONOUS TO TOUCH.

      4. Coarse, erect shrub up to 3 m. tall; buds dark brown, sessile; panicle ample, up to 20 cm. long; confined to swamps and wet shores; frequent, becoming sporadic northward.

R. vernix.

      4. Smaller, erect, trailing, or climbing by means of aerial rootlets; buds yellowish or tan-colored, often stalked; panicle compact, less than 8 cm. long; moist to dry sites; abundant throughout.

R. radicans*.

RIBES* (Pls. XXII and XXIII).

1. Armed.
   2. Twigs copiously prickly and bristly, yellowish and lustrous.

R. lacustre.

   2. Twigs armed with nodal spines or scattered internodal prickles or both (plant more or less densely prickly on older growth), grayish to brownish, opaque.
      3. Erect and arching, infrequent plant of rich, rocky woodlands.

R. cynosbati.

      3. Low, spreading or ascending, common plant of woods and clearings.

R. hirtellum.

1. Unarmed.
   4. Buds and branchlets bearing yellow resin dots (especially near apex).

R. americanum.

   4. Buds and branchlets without resin dots.
      5. Buds brown, less than 6 mm. long, with more than 5 scales; twigs not malodorous when bruised.

R. triste.

      5. Buds pinkish or reddish, the larger (especially terminal) up to 9 mm., with less than 5 scales; twigs malodorous when bruised or when epidermis scraped.

R. glandulosum.

ROBINIA (Pl. XXXIV).

1. Twigs bristly; shrubs less than 3 m. tall; infrequently escaping.

R. hispida.

1. Twigs not bristly, armed with paired nodal spines or unarmed; trees or large shrubs exceeding 3 m. in height; escaping occasionally to frequently.
   2. Twigs viscid, always armed with rather weak nodal spines; large shrub or small tree occasionally established near habitation.

R. viscosa

   2. Twigs not viscid, unarmed on slow, old growth or armed with stout spines on vigorous young growth; tree commonly established near habitation and spreading.

R. pseudo-acacia.

ROSA* (Pls. XXX & XXXI).

1. Twigs and larger spines pubescent, light tan-colored; fruit up to 2.5 cm. in diameter; frequently escaped and established, especially in sandy places.

R. rugosa.

1. Twigs and spines glabrous, reddish; fruit less than 1.5 cm. in diameter.
    2. Middle and upper internodes densely prickly.
        3. Rare plant of dry habitats; sepals persistent; receptacles and pedicels not bristly.

R. acicularis.

        3. Common plant of bogs; sepals deciduous; receptacles and pedicels bristly.

R. nitida.

    2. Middle and upper internodes unarmed, prickly only on vigorous growth.
        4. Inflorescence compound, many-branched, with several to many fruits; fruits less than 8 mm. in diameter; stem arching or trailing; escape.

R. multiflora.

        4. Inflorescence simple, few-branched with only a few fruits; fruits usually exceeding 8 mm. in diameter; stems erect to arching; natives.
            5. Vigorously growing twigs unarmed (plants more or less armed near base), frequently glaucous; sepals persistent in fruit; fruits and pedicels neither bristly nor with gland-tipped hairs.
                6. Sepals widely divergent or reflexed; plants local in northern Aroostook County.

R. johannensis.

                6. Sepals erect; plants common northward, frequent in southern portion of State.

R. blanda.

            5. Vigorously growing twigs armed.
                7. Low, less than 1 m. tall; nodal spines acicular; plant of dry areas.

R. carolina.

                7. Larger, exceeding 1 m. in height; nodal spines stouter, broad-based; plants of both wet and dry areas.
                    8. Nodal spines essentially straight to slightly hooked; plant of usually dry places, sometimes in damp habitats.

R. virginiana.

                    8. Nodal spines hooked; plant always of wet habitats.

R. palustris.

RUBUS (Pls. XXXII & XXXIII).

1. Prostrate or trailing.
    2. Armed with many bristles; leaves marcescent to persistent; twigs red.

R. hispidus.

    2. Unarmed; leaves deciduous; twigs brown.

R. pubescens.

1. Erect, arching, or doming.
    3. Twigs terete.
        4. Twigs unarmed, glandular-viscid; epidermis cracking and exfoliating.

R. odoratus.

        4. Twigs usually armed, not glandular-viscid; epidermis not cracking or exfoliating.
            5. Stems doming and rooting at tips, conspicuously glaucous, armed with scattered, stout prickles, but without bristles; frequent.

R. occidentalis.

            5. Stems erect or arching, not doming and rooting at tips, occasionally glaucous, armed with slender prickles or bristles or both or unarmed; abundant.

R. idaeus.

    3. Twigs prominently angled.
        6. Rachis of inflorescence bearing gland-tipped hairs; always armed.

R. allegheniensis.

        6. Rachis of inflorescence without gland-tipped hairs; sometimes unarmed.

R. canadensis.

29

SALIX (Pls. VIII - XIII)

1. Buds subopposite.

S. purpurea.

1. Buds alternate.
    2. Plants confined to arctic-alpine region of Mt. Katahdin.
        3. Plants up to 2.5 m. tall; buds up to 11 mm. long; twigs often glaucous.

S. planifolia.

        3. Plants less than 1 m. tall; buds less than 7 mm. long; twigs not glaucous.
            4. Plants prostrate, less than 1 dm. tall, the twigs horizontal or somewhat ascending.
                5. Twigs less than 2 cm. long and 1 mm. thick, bearing only a few buds, curving; main branches subterranean, rooting at nodes; infrequent.

S. herbacea.

                5. Twigs several to many cm. in length and exceeding 1 mm. in thickness, bearing several to many buds, straight; main branches above ground, not rooting at nodes; abundant.

S. uva-ursi.

            4. Plants spreading-ascending to erect, exceeding 1.5 dm. in height.
                6. Buds yellow-brown, usually red-glandular-dotted, less than 3.5 mm. long.

S. argyrocarpa.

                6. Buds dark purple, eglandular, up to 6 mm. long.

S. arctophila.

    2. Plants of lower elevations, not extending above tree line into arctic-alpine region of Mt. Katahdin.
        7. Twigs brittle, snapping off cleanly at junction with previous year's growth.
            8. Twigs and buds more or less pubescent.
                9. Bud scales appearing more or less sunken in upper portion.

S. lucida var. *intonsa.*

                9. Bud scales not collapsed above, the bud completely filling cavity made by its scale.
                    10. Buds less than 6 mm. long; common and locally abundant.

S. sericea.

                    10. Buds up to 10 mm. in length; local and infrequent.

S. coactilis.

            8. Twigs and buds glabrous.
                11. Buds less than 5 mm. long.
                    12. Buds acute; medium-sized shrub or small tree.

S. nigra.

                    12. Buds obtuse; shrub less than 1 m. tall.

S. lucida var. *angustifolia.*

                11. Buds, at least the larger, exceeding 5 mm. in length.
                    13. Buds and twigs highly lustrous; native shrub or small tree; common to abundant throughout the State.

S. lucida.

                    13. Buds and twigs only slightly lustrous; large tree escaping frequently south of latitude 45.5.

S. fragilis.*

        7. Twigs flexible at base.
            14. Stipule scars absent or inconspicuous.
                15. Shrubs exceeding 2 m. in height; frequent and locally abundant.
                    16. Buds broadest at base, usually yellow; twigs often glaucous; frequent and locally abundant along watercourses and bogs in the northern half of the State.

S. pellita.

                    16. Buds broadest above base, usually black or red (often 2-colored); twigs rarely glaucous, usually glabrous; common and locally abundant in wet meadows and swamps in the southern half of the State.

S. gracilis.

                15. Shrubs less than 1 m. tall; infrequent or rare.
                    17. Buds up to 7 mm. long; local, in acidic bogs.

S. pedicellaris.

17. Buds less than 4 mm. long; rare, on river banks.

S. interior.

14. Stipule scars conspicuous.
  18. Twigs and buds glabrous.
    19. Buds and twigs highly lustrous, appearing varnished; buds bright red.

S. pyrifolia.

    19. Buds and twigs dull to sublustrous.
      20. Buds often black or dark brown; flower buds much larger than vegetative buds, the larger flower buds exceeding 3.5 mm. in diameter.
        21. Local, rich riverbanks of northeastern Aroostook County.

S. glaucophylloides.

        21. Common to abundant throughout the State.

S. discolor.

      20. Buds lighter, brownish, reddish, or yellowish, not conspicuously differentiated into flower and vegetative buds, the larger less than 2.5 mm. in diameter.
        22. Common throughout State.

S. rigida.

        22. Infrequent in northern Aroostook County.

S. cordata var. *abrasa.*

  18. Twigs and sometimes buds more or less pubescent.
    23. Buds and twigs densely covered with flocculent tomentum; rare and local shrub of calcareous bogs of northern Aroostook County; plant not exceeding 2 m. in height.

S. candida.

    23. Buds and twigs merely pubescent; frequent to abundant shrubs exceeding 2 m. in height or trees.
      24. Buds of uniform size.
        25. Trees; escapes.
          26. Buds ovoid; twigs often densely pubescent; common in and apparently restricted to southeastern Washington County.

X *S. smithiana.*

          26. Buds ovoid-oblong; twigs usually sparsely pubescent; infrequent throughout the State.

S. alba*.

        25. Shrubs; native.
          27. 0.3-1.5 m. tall; common in Aroostook County.

S. cordata.

          27. 0.3-3 m. tall; infrequent throughout State.

S. rigida f. *mollis.*

      24. Buds of 2 distinct sizes.
        28. Buds and twigs uniformly reddish-orange or reddish-pink.

S. bebbiana.

        28. Buds and twigs variously colored but not uniformly reddish-orange.
          29. Plants 0.3-6 m. tall; infrequent.

S. discolor var. *latifolia.*

          29. Plants 0.3-3 m. tall; common.

S. humilis.

SAMBUCUS (Pl. LXI).

1. Pith orange-brown; buds ovoid, large.

S. pubens*.

1. Pith white; buds conical, small.

S. canadensis.

SPIRAEA (Pl. XXXIII).

1. Twigs glabrous, brown; panicles open, pyramidal.

S. latifolia*

1. Twigs tomentose, purplish underneath tomentum; panicles compact.

S. tomentosa.

31

VACCINIUM (Pls. LIV-LVI).

1. Leaves persistent; plants low, trailing or prostrate; fruit a commonly persistent red berry.
  2. Leaves obovate, bearing minute dark bristles below; peduncles short; plant of exposed rocky or dry peaty areas.

V. vitis-idaea var. *minus.*

  2. Leaves broadest at or below middle, glabrous below; peduncles up to 5 cm. long; plants of bogs or wet areas.
    3. Leaves elliptical, rounded at apex, 6-17 mm. long; peduncles lateral, bearing 2 bracts 4-10 mm. long toward apex; berry 1-2 cm. in diameter.

V. macrocarpon.

    3. Leaves triangular to ovate-oblong, pointed at apex, 6-15 mm. long; peduncles terminal (as evidenced by jog in stem), bearing 2 bracts 1-2.5 mm. long below middle; berry 5-10 mm. in diameter.

V. oxycoccos.*

1. Leaves deciduous; plants erect to spreading-ascending; fruit rarely persistent.
  4. Bud scales 2; stems short, less than 2 dm. long.

V. cespitosum.

  4. Bud scales more than 2; stems exceeding 2 dm. in length.
    5. Twigs not papillose; buds blunt, not differentiated into flower and vegetative buds; epidermis brown, exfoliating.

V. uliginosum var. *alpinum.*

    5. Twigs papillose; buds acute to acuminate, differentiated into flower and vegetative (smaller) buds; epidermis green, red, or black, not exfoliating.
      6. Plants 2-20 dm. tall.
        7. Twigs conspicuously pubescent.

V. myrtilloides.

        7. Twigs glabrous to sparsely pubescent.
          8. Abundant.

V. angustifolium var. *laevifolium*.*

          8. Local.

V. vacillans.

      6. Plants 1-4 m. tall.
        9. Twigs and branchlets often sooty-pubescent.

V. atrococcum.

        9. Twigs and branchlets glabrous or with light-colored hairs.
          10. Common.

V. corymbosum.

          10. Local.

V. caesariense.

VIBURNUM (Pls. LXII & LXIII).

1. Buds naked.

V. alnifolium.

1. Buds scaly.
  2. Bud scales 2, appearing as 1; fruit a persistent, red drupe.
    3. Buds dark purple; inflorescence few-flowered; stones of drupes averaging 5 mm. broad and 7 mm. long; local plant of cold, moist areas of higher elevations.

V. edule.

    3. Buds reddish; inflorescence many-flowered; stones of drupes averaging 7 mm. broad and 9 mm. long; common plant of lowlands.

V. trilobum.

  2. Bud scales 2 or more, clearly distinct; fruit rarely persistent.
    4. Bud scales 2, valvate; buds linear, scurfy.
      5. Buds purple; scales of terminal bud valvate for their entire length; branches of inflorescence arising from apex of the peduncle.

V. lentago.

5. Buds tan-colored, scales of terminal bud often not meeting along their edges at base, exposing flower bud within; branches of inflorescence not arising from apex of the peduncle, borne directly on apex of twig.

V. cassinoides.

4. Bud scales more than 2; buds ovoid, not scurfy.
   6. Twigs angled, glabrous; buds brown.

V. recognitum.

   6. Twigs terete, more or less pubescent, buds often purplish.

V. acerifolium.

VITIS (Pl. XLIII).

1. Tendrils or vestiges or scars of inflorescence present at each of 3-7 successive nodes.

V. labrusca.

1. Tendrils or vestiges or scars of inflorescence usually absent from every third node.

V. riparia and *V. novae-angliae.*

NOTES FROM SPECIES KEY
(Listed alphabetically by genus)

Betula lutea (*B. alleghaniensis*):
    a. Bracts of strobili 5-8 mm. long; common.

                                      B. lutea.

    a. Bracts of strobili 8-13 mm. long; occasional.

                              B. l. var. *macrolepis.*

Betula papyrifera:
    a. Bark of mature trunks white.
        b. Mature bracts of strobili 3.5-7 mm. long
            c. Twigs spreading or ascending; common.

                              B. papyrifera.

            c. Twigs pendulous, occasional.

                          B. p. var. *pensilis.*

        b. Mature bracts 7-10 mm. long; known only from Aroostook County.

                       B. p. var. *macrostachya.*

    a. Bark of mature trunks warm brown to creamy white.
        d. Bracts 5-10 mm. long.

                          B. p. var. *cordifolia.*

        d. Bracts 3.5-7 mm. long.

                       B. p. var. *commutata.*

Fraxinus pennsylvanica consists of three intergrading varieties.

Hudsonia tomentosa var. *intermedia* may be separated from var. *tomentosa* on the basis of the more evident, often projecting leaf apices of the former.

Ilex verticillata:
    a. Branchlets dark brown.

              I. verticillata and *I. v.* var. *padifolia.*

    a. Branchlets pale.
        b. Twigs divergent.

                          I. v. var. *tenuifolia.*

        b. Twigs strongly ascending, fastigiate.

                          I. v. var. *fastigiata.*

Lonicera villosa:
    a. Twigs glabrous.

                            L. v. var. *tonsa.*

    a. Twigs pubescent.
        b. Twigs tomentose.

                                L. villosa.

        b. Twigs puberulent.
             c. Twigs puberulent and with some scattered long, soft or coarse hairs.

                          L. v. var. *solonis.*

            c. Twigs merely puberulent.

                       L. v. var. *calvescens.*

Pinus rigida:
    a. Cones 3-7 cm. long; plant arborescent, common.

                                P. rigida.

    a. Cones 4.5-5.5 cm. long; plant shrubby, compact, infrequent.

                          P. r. f. *globosa.*

Populus tremuloides:
    a. Twigs of uniform thickness, not swollen, flexible at base; nodes remote.
        b. Twigs spreading or ascending.

                            P. tremuloides.

        b. Twigs pendulous.

                          P. t. f. *pendula.*

    a. Twigs irregularly swollen, often brittle at base; nodes approximate.

                         P. t. var. *magnifica.*

Potentilla tridendata:
   a. Leaflets glabrous.

P. tridentata.

   a. Leaflets hirsute.

P. t. f. *hirsutifolia.*

Quercus rubra:
   a. Bark of upper trunk and branches dark gray or brown.

Q. rubra.

   a. Bark of upper trunk and branches pale gray.

Q. r. var. *borealis.*

Rhus glabra:
   a. Twigs essentially glabrous.

R. glabra.

   a. Twigs puberulent.

R. g. var. *borealis.*

Rhus radicans: A highly variable plant, particularly in habit. South of latitude 45, the plant may or may not develop aerial rootlets. North of latitude 45, it does not develop rootlets. In sterile habitats, the plant is often low (less than 2 dm. tall) and sprawling, while it may reach 1.5 m. in height in rich areas such as alluvial bottomlands or rich rocky woods.

Ribes: A few species (especially *R. sativum*) frequently persist and spread from plantings near houses or old house sites.

Rosa: Several species (especially *R. cinnamomea, R. eglanteria,* and *R. spinosissima*) frequently persist and spread from plantings near houses or old house sites.

Sambucus pubens:
   a. Twigs pubescent.

S. pubens.

   a. Twigs glabrous.

S. p. f. *calva.*

Spiraea latifolia:
   a. Panicles open, pyramidal; plant up to 2 m. in height and common at low elevations.

S. latifolia.

   a. Panicles compact, ovoid to cylindric; plant less than 0.7 m. tall and confined to arctic-alpine regions of Mt. Katahdin.

S. l. var. *septentrionalis.*

Vaccinium angustifolium is a low, delicate shrub usually found in exposed habitats such as ledges. It is distinguished from its three varieties (the most common of which is *V. a.* var. *laevifolium*) on the basis of their greater size.

Abscission. (abscising). Development of a weak band of tissue near the base of the petiole or stalk to allow for separation of leaves and other parts at the end of the growing season.

Acicular. Needle-shaped.

Acidic. Acid-forming; of low pH.

Acuminate. Tapering to a long, sharp point.

Acute. Sharp-pointed.

Aggregate. A compound fruit formed by the collection of simple fruits into a distinct structure (Pl. XXXIII).

Alternate. Said of leaves, buds and leaf scars placed singly at different points on the twig or branchlet.

Ample. Full, expansive.

Anastomosing. Said of ridges of bark regularly inter-weaving and interlacing.

Angiospermae. Subdivision of seed-plants in which the ovule or ovules are enclosed in an ovary which matures into a fruit.

Apical. At the summit or tip.

Appressed. Closely pressed against.

Approximate. Close to one another.

Armature. Any occurrence of bristles, prickles, spines or thorns on any part of the plant.

Ascending. Rising somewhat obliquely; curving upward.

Autotrophic. Making their own nutritive substances by photosynthesis.

Axillary. Situated in the upper angle between bud or leaf scar and twig or branchlet.

Baccate. Berry-like.

Basipetal. Developing in a longitudinal plane from an apical point toward the base.

Berry. A fleshy or pulpy simple fruit with usually many seeds (Pl. LIV, 1c, 2c, 3c).

Biennial. Living for two growing seasons.

Branchlet. Persistent growth of the past few years ex-cluding the growth of the previous growing season (see Twig).

Bristle. A stiff, strong hair.

Bud. A rudimentary twig or inflorescence either covered by scales or naked, generally axillary (less often superposed or collateral), pseudoterminal, or terminal and either wholly vegetative or wholly floral (usually larger than vegetative) or mixed.

Bundle scars. Scars of vascular tissue formed by abscission, found within the leaf scar.

Calcareous. Limy, having a high pH as a result of the presence of calcium.

Calciphyte. A plant which grows in a calcareous soil.

Calyx (pl. *calyces*). Outer whorl or cycle of parts of a flower, sometimes persisting in fruit (Pl. LIV, 4c).

Capitate. Collected into a dense cluster or head (Pl. LIX, 1a).

Capsule. A dry, simple fruit maturing from a compound ovary (more than 1 carpel), dehiscing at maturity into two or more valves. (Pl. L, 2c).

Catkin (overwintering). The preformed inflorescence of some members of the Myricaceae and Corylaceae; either of two different sizes (then the staminate larger than pistillate, e.g. *Alnus rugosa, A. serrulata*) or uniform and staminate; distinguished from vegetative or mixed (floral and vegetative) buds by greater size and generally apical location (Pls. XIV-XVIII).

Cespitose. Tufted, clustered together.

Chambered (of pith). Broken into cavities by evenly-spaced, horizontal partitions (Pl. XIV, 4).

Chartaceous. Papery.

Collateral (of buds). Situated beside the axillary bud, which is centered over the leaf scar (Pl. XL, 1 & 2).

Compound. Composed of two or more similar parts united into one whole.

Conduplicate. Folded together lengthwise.

Confluent. Merging together.

Connate. United or joined.

Coriaceous. Leathery.

Corymb. A modified raceme in which the length of pedicels increases basipetally making the whole struc-ture flat-topped or convex (Pl. L).

Crenate. Bearing rounded teeth.

Cyme. A broad, flattish-topped inflorescence (differs from a corymb in blooming sequence) (Pl. XLVI).

Deciduous. Falling from a plant as a result of abscission; opposite of persistent.

Decumbent. Prostrate, but with an ascending apex.

Decurrent. Extending downward from the point of origin.

Dehiscent (*dehiscence*). Opening along lines or sutures into valves.

Deltoid. Triangular.

Dentate. With pointed, outwardly-projecting teeth.

Denticulate. Minutely dentate.

Depressed. Giving the appearance of being flattened from above.

Diaphragmed. A solid pith having regularly-spaced horizontal partitions (Pl. XLVII, 3).

Diffuse-porous. Said of porous (angiosperm) wood in which the pores (vessels) exhibit no discernable varia-tion in size throughout the season's growth. (Make cross-section of twig or stem.)

Dimorphic. Occurring in two forms.

Discoid. Disc-shaped.

Distichous (of buds, leaf scars). Two-ranked, alternate and arranged in two rows, having a phyllotaxis of ½.

Divaricate. Widely divergent.

Divergent. Spreading broadly.

Dorsal. Relating to the back or outer surface.

Drupe (*drupaceous*). A fleshy simple fruit with usually one or a few stony pits (Pl. XXXVII, 1d, 2d, 3d).

Eglandular. Lacking glands.

Elliptical. Rounded equally at both ends and broadest near the middle.

Emarginate. With a shallow notch at the apex.

Entire. Without teeth or lobes.

Erose. Said of a margin which appears eroded or gnawed into small, irregular sections (Pl. III, 3e).

Excavated (of pith). Hollow (Pl. LXI, 3, 4, 5, & 6).

Exfoliating. Peeling off in thin layers (Pl. XXVI, 1).

Fascicle. A dense cluster or bundle (Pl. IV).

Fastigiate. With branches growing erect and close together.

Flocculent. Covered with soft wool or hair.

Floricane. The second year's aerial growth in the biennial *Rubus;* it consists of vegetative growth and flowering which are followed by death of the stem at the end of the growing season. (Pl. XXXII). See *Primocane.*

Follicle. A dry simple fruit opening along one suture (Pl. XXXIII, 1c, 2c, 3c).

Fruit. The seed-bearing organ of a plant.

Fusiform. Spindle-shaped, narrowing toward both ends from a swollen middle.

Glabrescent. Becoming glabrous.

Glabrous. Not hairy.

Glaucous. Covered and whitened by a powdery or waxy substance which rubs off.

Globose. Spherical.

Glutinous. Sticky.

Gymnospermae. Subdivision of seed-plants in which the ovule or ovules are naked, not enclosed in an ovary.

Habit. The general appearance or manner of growth of a plant.

Habitat. The type of environment which a plant frequents.

Hip. Fruit of the genus *Rosa* in which the receptacle forms an urn-shaped container enclosing the bony achenes (Pls. XXX and XXXI).

Hirsute. Bearing rather rough or coarse hairs.

Hoary. Covered with a close white or whitish pubescence.

Homogeneous (of pith). Of uniform texture, not interrupted by partitions.

Imbricate. Overlapping.

Inflorescence. The flowering and fruiting portion of a plant.

Internodal. Occurring between nodes.

Lanceolate. Lance-shaped; much longer than broad; widest below the middle and tapering to the apex.

Leaf scar. The scar left by leaf abscission, usually evident just below a bud (see Pl. XXXIV, 1, 2, 3) and containing one or more bundle scars.

Legume. A dry simple fruit of the Fabaceae opening along two sutures. (Pl. XXXIV, 3).

Lenticel (*lenticellate*). A small corky protuberance on the bark of twigs and branchlets which allows for gaseous exchange between inner tissues and the air (Pl. LXI, 1 & 2).

Ligulate (of bracts). Strap-shaped.

Linear. Long and narrow, the sides nearly parallel.

Locule. The compartment or cavity of an ovary.

Lorate (of leaves). Strap-shaped.

Lunate. Of the shape of a half-moon or crescent.

Lustrous. Shiny.

Malodorous. Ill-smelling.

Marcescent. Withering but persistent.

Mast year. A year of high fruit production.

Membranaceous. Thin and more or less soft and pliable.

Mixed (of buds). Containing both vegetative and floral rudiments; usually larger than vegetative buds.

Mucronate. Ending in an abrupt, small, and sharp point.

Multiple (of fruit). One composed of the ripened ovaries of many separate flowers on the same axis (Pl. XXIV, 4c).

Naked (of buds). Lacking bud scales (Pl. XXIV, 3b).

Node. The point on a twig which bears one or more leaves or leaf scars.

Nutlet. A small nut.

Ob-. Latin prefix usually signifying inversion. For example, obovate means egg-shaped but broadest above the middle.

Oblong. Two or three times longer than broad and with nearly parallel sides.

Obtuse. Blunt or rounded at the end.

Opaque. Dull, not shining.

Opposite. Two at a node, on opposite sides of the axis, twig, or branchlet.

Orbicular. Circular.

Oval. Broadly elliptical.

Ovate. Having the outline of a hen's egg, with the broader end basal.

Ovoid.   A solid with an ovate outline.

Ovuliferous.   Bearing ovules.

Oxylophyte.   A plant which inhabits acidic soil.

Panicle.   A modified raceme in which the branches from the rachis are themselves branched. (Pl. XXXIII, 1a, 2a, 3a).

Paniculate.   Resembling a panicle.

Papillose.   Covered by minute pebbly or nipple-shaped projections.

Pedicel.   The stalk of one flower or fruit in an inflorescence.

Peduncle.   The stalk of an inflorescence or of one fruit if the inflorescence consists of only 1 fruit.

Peltate.   Attached by a central stalk.

Pendulous.   Drooping, hanging down.

Perennial.   Living for three or more years.

Petiole.   Leaf stalk.

Phyllotaxis.   The arrangement of leaves, buds or leaf scars on the twig or branchlet; expressed as a fraction, the numerator representing the number of revolutions of a spiral made in passing from one leaf past each successive leaf to reach the leaf directly above the initial leaf, and the demoninator representing the number of leaves passed in the spiral.

Pinnatifid.   Said of a leaf which is cleft or deeply divided perpendicular to the mid-vein. (Pl. XIV, 1).

Pistillate.   Provided with ovaries.

Pith.   The central region of a twig, usually spongy and clearly contrasting with the surrounding tissue in texture; either homogeneous, chambered, diaphragmed, or excavated.

Plane.   With a flat surface.

Plano-convex.   Flat on one surface and convex on the opposite surface.

Pome.   Fruit of certain members of the Rosaceae such as apple; core fruit (Pl. XXVII, 2).

Prickle.   A weak, slender, sharp outgrowth of the epidermis or bark.

Primocane.   The first year's aerial growth in the biennial *Rubus;* it consists of vegetative growth, except for the formation of flower buds which bloom in the second year (Pl. XXXII). See *Floricane.*

Procumbent.   Lying on the ground or trailing but not rooting at the nodes.

Prostrate.   Lying flat on the ground.

Pseudoterminal.   Said of buds at the apex of the twig which are falsely terminal; the last formed lateral bud, typically situated between the leaf scar and twig scar (Pl. XVII, 1b, 2b, 4b).

Puberulent.   Minutely pubescent, the hairs scarcely visible to the unaided eye.

Pubescent.   Covered with short, soft hairs; hairy.

Raceme.   An inflorescence consisting of an elongate rachis and pedicelled flowers (Pl. XXXII, 2c, 5c).

Racemose.   In racemes or resembling a raceme.

Rachis.   The axis of an inflorescence.

Receptacle.   The more or less expanded apical portion of the pedicel or peduncle upon which flower and fruit are borne.

Reflexed.   Abruptly bent or curved downward.

Remote.   Distant from one another, not close or crowded.

Revolute.   With margin rolled toward the lower side (Pl. XLVIII, 3a).

Ring-porous.   Said of porous (angiosperm) wood in which the pores (vessels) formed at the beginning of the growing season are much larger than those formed later, usually resulting in an abrupt transition between season's growths. (Make cross-section of twig or stem.)

Rufous.   Reddish-brown.

Rugose.   Wrinkled.

Rugulose.   Minutely or finely rugose.

Samara.   An indehiscent, winged fruit (Pls. XXXIX, XL, LVII).

Scale.   A modified leaf of bract.

Scaly (of buds).   Covered by one or more scales.

Scarious.   Thin, dry, and membranaceous, not green.

Scurfy.   Covered by minute scale-like or bran-like particles.

Sepal.   A segment or division of the calyx.

Sericeous.   Silky.

Serrate.   Having sharp, foward-pointed teeth.

Serrulate.   Minutely serrate.

Sessile.   Not stalked.

Seta (pl. *setae*).   A bristle.

Setulose.   Bearing minute bristles.

Shrub.   Any woody plant smaller than a tree and usually consisting of several stems rather than a single trunk.

Sinus.   The space between two adjacent lobes of a leaf.

Simple.   Said of a leaf not compounded into separate leaflets; of an inflorescence which is not branched; and of a fruit maturing from one ovary.

Solid (of pith).   Not hollow.

Solitary.   Borne singly.

Spatulate.   Gradually narrowed toward the base from a rounded summit.

Spiciform.   Spike-like.

Spike.   A modified raceme in which the pedicels are suppressed making the flowers sessile.

Spine.   A sharp, woody outgrowth of the stem. (See "thorn".)

Spinescent.   Ending in a spine.

Staminate. Provided with stamens.

Stellate. Said of a 5-pointed pith or of hairs which radiate from a common point (Pls. VII; VIII 1 & 2; XX; XXI; XLVII, 1d).

Stipule. A more or less leaf-like or spine-like structure occurring in pairs at the base of the petiole (Pl. XXXIII, 4).

Stipule scars. Scars left by the stipules, usually one on each side of the leaf scar (Pl. XVIII).

Stoloniferous. Producing roots from basal branches or runners.

Stoma (Pl. *stomata*). One of numerous, minute openings in the leaf providing for controlled exchange of gases between inner tissue and the air.

Striate. Marked with fine longitudinal lines (Pl. XVIII, 2b, 2c).

Strigose. Beset with straight and stiff appressed hairs.

Strobilus. A cone-like fruiting inflorescence with imbricate bracts upon which are borne the seeds (Gymnospermae) or the fruits (Angiospermae) (Pls. XVI & XVII).

Sub-. Latin prefix meaning somewhat, slightly or rather.

Subopposite. Said of buds which are distinctly paired but not directly opposite one another; characteristic of *Rhamnus cathartica* (Pl. XLI, 2a) and *Salix purpurea* (Pl. VIII, 3a) and, occasionally in fast-growing twigs of species with normally strictly opposite phyllotaxis.

Subulate. Awl-shaped, long-tapering from base to apex (Pl. LIII, 3).

Sulcate. Grooved or furrowed.

Superposed (of buds). Situated directly above the axillary bud (Pls. XXIV, 1; XIV, 4).

Suture. A line of opening or dehiscence.

Tendril. A slender, elongate modification of leaf or stem by which a plant grasps an object and clings to it for support (Pls. VI, 3; XLII; XLIII).

Terete. Having a circular cross-section.

Thorn. A sharp, rigid, spine-like twig or branchlet; distringuished from a spine by its greater size and position in the axil of a leaf scar.

Tomentose. Covered by a dense, matted woolly pubescence.

Tomentulose. Minutely tomentose.

Tree. A woody plant exceeding 20 feet in height and usually with a single trunk and a definite crown.

Trifoliolate. Bearing three leaflets (Pls. XXVI, 3; XXXIII, 4).

Truncate. Appearing as if cut off at the end.

Twig. The growth of the previous growing season; determined by progressing down the stem from the apex to the first abrupt change in color or texture, this point usually marked by scars from the tip bud of the previous winter.

Umbel. A modified raceme in which all the pedicels arise from a common point (Pl. XLVIII, 3b).

Umbo. A protuberance from either the apex or the dorsal surface near the apex of a gymnospermous cone which may or may not be armed.

Valvate (of buds). Meeting along their margins but not overlapping (Pls. XL, 3, 4; XLVI; LXII, 1, 2).

Valve. One of the segments into which a capsule dehisces.

Variegated. Marked by distinct light-colored areas strongly contrasting with the dominant color (Pls. LIX, 4; XLVII, 1).

Vascular. Referring to specialized conductive tissue.

Vestiture. Any king of hairiness.

Villous. Covered with long, soft hairs.

Vinaceous. Of the color of dark red wine.

Vine. A plant which climbs upon another plant or upon some object by twining or by some specialized device such as tendrils or aerial rootlets.

Viscid. Glutinous; sticky.

Whorled. Occurring three or more at a node.

REFERENCES

Bean, R. C., C. D. Richards, and F. Hyland. 1966. Revised Check-list of the Vascular Plants of Maine. Bulletin of the Josselyn Botanical Society of Maine, Orono.

Fernald, M. L. 1950. *Gray's Manual of Botany.* Eighth edition. American Book Co., New York.

Graves, A. H. 1956. *Illustrated Guide to Trees and Shrubs.* Revised edition. Harper and Row, Publishers Inc., New York.

Harlow, W. M. and E. S. Harrar. 1969. *Textbook of Dendrology.* Fifth edition. McGraw-Hill Book Co., New York.

Hodgdon, A. R., and F. L. Steele. 1966. *Rubus* Subgenus *Eubatus* In New England, A Conspectus. Rhodora, Vol. 68.

Hyland, F. (reprinted 1974). Conifers of Maine, Bulletin 345 revised University of Maine Press, Orono.

———, and F. H. Steinmetz. 1944. *The Woody Plants of Maine.* University of Maine Press, Orono.

Lawrence, G. H. M. 1951. *Taxonomy of Vascular Plants.* Macmillian Company, New York.

Manley, S. A. M. 1971. Identification of Red, Black, and Hybrid Spruces. Department of the Environment, Canadian Forestry Service Publication No. 1301, Ottawa.

Muenscher, W. C. 1969. *Keys to Woody Plants.* Sixth edition, revised. Comstock Publishing Asscoiates, Ithaca.

Otis, C. H. 1970 (revised eighteenth printing, original copyright in 1931). *Michigan Trees.* University of Michigan Press.

Rehder, Alfred. 1940. *Manual of Cultivated Trees and Shrubs.* Second edition. Macmillan Company, New York.

Sargent, C. S. 1961. *Manual of the Trees of North America.* Second edition. Reprinted by Dover Publications, Inc., New York.

Trelease, W. 1967. *Winter Botany.* Third edition. Reprinted by Dover Publications, New York.

Wiegand, K. M. and F. W. Foxworthy. 1908. *A Key to Genera of Woody Plants in Winter.* Third edition, Cornell University Press, Ithaca.

INDEX TO LATIN AND COMMON NAMES
(followed by their equivalents, if they exist, in parentheses)

NOTE: Page and plate numbers are given only after the latin names of the plants. Therefore, knowing only the common name, one may locate the plant in the text and plates by referring to the latin name equivalent following its common name.

Atlantic White-cedar (*Chamaecyparis thyoides*)

Azalea (*Rhododendron*)
  Alpine- (*R. lapponicum*)
  Clammy (*R. viscosum*)

Balm of Gilead (X *Populus gileadensis*)

Balsam
  Fir (*Abies balsamea*)
  Poplar (*Populus balsamifera*)
  Willow (*Salix pyrifolia*)

Barberry (*Berberis*)
  Common (*B. vulgaris*)
  Japanese (*B. thunbergii*)

Basswood (*Tilia americana*)
  American (*T. americana*)

Bayberry (*Myrica pensylvanica*)

Beach Plum (*Prunus maritima*)

Beaked Hazelnut (*Corylus cornuta*)

Bearberry (*Arctostaphylos*)
  Alpine (*A. alpina*)
  Willow (*Salix uva-ursi*)

Bear Oak (*Quercus ilicifolia*)

Bebb Willow (*Salix bebbiana*)

Beech
  American (*Fagus grandifolia*)
  Blue (*Carpinus caroliniana* var. *virginiana*)
  Water- (*C. caroliniana* var. *virginiana*)

Berberis (Barberry), 12, 21, Pl. XXII
  thunbergii DC. (Japanese Barberry), 21, Pl. XXII
  vulgaris L. (Common Barberry), 21, Pl. XXII

Berry
  June- (*Amelanchier*)
  Male- (*Lyonia ligustrina*)
  Nanny- (*Viburnum lentago*)
  Partridge- (*Mitchella repens*)
  Russet Buffalo- (*Shepherdia canadensis*)
  Sarvice- (*Amelanchier*)
  Service- (*Amelanchier*)

Betula (Birch), 2, 15, 16, 21, 22, 34, Pls. XVI & XVII
  caerulea-grandis Blanch. (Blue Birch), 21, Pl. XVII
  glandulosa Michx. (Dwarf Birch), 20, Pl. XVI
  lenta L. (Cherry, Sweet, or Black Birch), 20, Pl. XVI
  lutea Michx. f. (Yellow), 20, 34, Pl. XVI
    var. *macrolepis* Fern., 34
  minor (Tuckerm.) Fern. (Dwarf White Birch), 20, Pl. XVI
  papyrifera Marsh. (White, Paper, or Canoe Birch), 21, 34, Pl. XVII
    var. *commutata* (Regel) Fern., 34
    var. *cordifolia* (Regel) Fern. (Mountain Paper Birch), 34
    var. *macrostachya* Fern., 34
    var. *pensilis* Fern., 34
  populifolia Marsh. (Gray, Old-field, Poverty, or

Getchell Birch), 21, Pl. XVII
  pumila L. (Low or Swamp Birch), 20, Pl. XVII

Big-tooth Aspen (*Populus grandidentata*)

Birch (*Betula*)
  Black (*B. lenta*)
  Blue (*B. caerulea-grandis*)
  Canoe (*B. papyrifera*)
  Cherry (*B. lenta*)
  Dwarf (*B. glandulosa*)
  White (*B. minor*)
  Getchell (*B. populifolia*)
  Gray (*B. populifolia*)
  Low (*B. pumila*)
  Mountain Paper (*B. papyrifera* var. *cordifolia*)
  Old-field (*B. populifolia*)
  Paper (*B. papyrifera*)
  Poverty (*B. populifolia*)
  Swamp (*B. pumila*)
  Sweet (*B. lenta*)
  White (*B. papyrifera*)
  Yellow (*B. lutea*)

Bird Cherry (*Prunus pensylvanica*)

Bitter nightshade (*Solanum dulcamara*)

Bittersweet
  Climbing (*Celastrus scandens*)
  European (*Solanum dulcamara*)
  Shrubby (*Celastrus scandens*)

Black
  Ash (*Fraxinus nigra*)
  Birch (*Betula lenta*)
  Cherry (*Prunus serotina*)
  Crowberry (*Empetrum nigrum*)
  Currant, Swamp (*Ribes lacustre*)
  Currant, Wild (*R. americanum*)
  Highbush Blueberry (*Vaccinium caesariense*)
  Huckleberry (*Gaylussacia baccata*)
  Locust (*Robinia pseudo-acacia*)
  Oak (*Quercus velutina*)
  Raspberry (*Rubus occidentalis*)
  Spruce (*Picea mariana*)
  Tupelo (*Nyssa sylvatica*)
  Willow (*Salix nigra*)

Black-alder (*Ilex verticillata*)

Black-berried Elder (*Sambucus canadensis*)

Black-fruited Chokeberry (*Pyrus melanocarpa*)

Black-gum (*Nyssa sylvatica*)

Blackberry (*Rubus allegheniensis*)
  Smooth (*R. canadensis*)

Blue
  Birch (*Betula caerulea-grandis*)
  Dogwood (*Cornus alternifolia*)

Blue-beech (*Carpinus caroliniana* var. *virginiana*)

Blueberry (*Vaccinium*)
  Black Highbush (*V. atrococcum*)
  Canada (*V. myrtilloides*)

Elm (Ulmus)
   American (*U. americana*)
   Red (*U. rubra*)
   Slippery (*U. rubra*)
   White (*U. americana*)
Empetrum (Crowberry) 6, 7, 23, Pl. XXXV
   atropurpureum Fern. & Wieg. (Red Crowberry), 23,
      Pl. XXXV
   nigrum L. (Black Crowberry), 23, Pl. XXXV
Epigaea repens L. var. *glabrifolia* Fern. (Trailing
      Arbutus, Mayflower) 8, Pl. LIII
European
   Bittersweet (*Solanum dulcamara*)
   Fly Honeysuckle (*Lonicera xylosteum*)
   Mountain-ash (*Pyrus aucuparia*)
Fagus grandifolia Ehrh. (American Beech), 8, 17, Pl.
      XIX
False-spiraea
   Ural (*Sorbaria sorbifolia*)
Fern
   Sweet (*Comptonia peregrina*)
Fever-bush (*Lindera benzoin*)
Fir
   Balsam (*Abies balsamea*)
Fire Cherry (*Prunus pensylvanica*)
Flowering
   Dogwood (*Cornus florida*)
   Raspberry, Purple (*Rubus odoratus*)
Fly Honeysuckle
   American (*Lonicera canadensis*)
   European (*L. xylosteum*)
   Mountain (*L. villosa*)
   Swamp (*L. oblongifolia*)
Fox Grape
   Northern (*Vitis labrusca*)
Fraxinus (Ash), 10, 23, 34, Pl. LVII
   americana L. (White Ash), 23, Pl. LVII
   nigra Marsh. (Black), 23, Pl. LVII
   pennsylvanica Marsh. (Red, Green Ash), 23, 34, Pl.
      LVII
Frost Grape (*Vitis riparia*)
Gale
   Sweet (*Myrica gale*)
Garden Red Current (*Ribes sativum*)
Gaultheria, 7, 8, 23, Pl. LIII
   hispidula (L.) Bigel. (Creeping Snowberry, Moxie-
      plum, Capillaire), 8, 23, Pl. LIII
   procumbens L. (Teaberry, Checkerberry), 7, 23, Pl.
      LIII
Gaylussacia (Huckleberry), 15, 23, Pl. LV
   baccata (Wang.) K. Koch (Black Huckleberry), 23,
      Pl. LV
   dumosa (Andr.) T. & G. var. *bigeloviana* Fern. (Dwarf
      Huckleberry), 23, Pl. LV
Glaucous Willow (*Salix discolor*)

Gooseberry (*Ribes*)
   Prickly (*R. cynosbati*)
   Smooth (*R. hirtellum*)
Goose-foot Maple (*Acer pensylvanicum*)
Grape (*Vitis*)
   Frost (*V. riparia*)
   New England (*V. novae-angliae*)
   Northern Fox (*V. labrusca*)
   Pilgrim (*V. novae-angliae*)
   River-bank (*V. riparia*)
Gray
   Birch (*Betula populifolia*)
   Dogwood (*Cornus racemosa*)
Great-laurel (*Rhododendron maximum*)
Green Ash (*Fraxinus pennsylvanica*)
Greenbrier
   Common (*Smilax rotundifolia*)
Ground Juniper (*Juniperus communis* var. *depressa*)
Ground-hemlock (*Taxus canadensis*)
Ground-pink (*Phlox subulata*)
Gum
   Black- (*Nyssa sylvatica*)
   Sour- (*N. sylvatica*)

Hamamelis virginiana L. (Witch-hazel), 13, Pl. XXIV
Hard Maple (*Acer saccharum*)
Hardhack (*Spiraea tomentosa*)
Hazelnut (*Corylus*)
   American (*C. americana*)
   Beaked (*C. cornuta*)
Heath
   Mountain (*Phyllodoce caerulea*)
Heath-like Hudsonia (*Hudsonia ericoides*)
Heather (*Calluna vulgaris*)
Hemlock
   Eastern (*Tsuga canadensis*)
   Ground- (*Taxus canadensis*)
Hickory
   Shagbark (*Carya ovata*)
Highbush
   Blueberry (*Vaccinium corymbosum*)
   Blueberry, Black (*V. atrococcum*)
   Cranberry (*Viburnum trilobum*)
Hoary
   Willow (*Salix candida*)
Hobble
   Witch (*Viburnum alnifolium*)
Hobble-bush (*Viburnum alnifolium*)
Holly
   Mountain (*Nemopanthus mucronata*)
Honeysuckle (*Lonicera*)
   American Fly (*L. canadensis*)
   Bush- (*Diervilla lonicera*)
   Climbing (*L. dioica*)
   European Fly (*L. xylosteum*)
   Morrow (*L. morrowi*)

46

Sweet Blueberry (*Vaccinium angustifolium*)
Lowbush blueberry (*Vaccinium angustifolium*)
Lycium chinense Mill. (Matrimony-vine), 11, 12, 14, Pl. LVIII
Lyonia ligustrina (L.) DC. (Male-berry), 15, Pl. XLVIII

Male-berry (*Lyonia ligustrina*)
Maple (*Acer*)
    Ash-leaved (*A. negundo*)
    Goose-foot (*A. pensylvanicum*)
    Hard (*A. saccharum*)
    Mountain (*A. spicatum*)
    Norway (*A. platanoides*);
    Red (*A. rubrum*)
    Rock (*A. saccharum*)
    Silver (*A. saccharinum*)
    Striped (*A. pensylvanicum*)
    Sugar (*A. saccharum*)
    White (*A. saccharinum*)
Maple-leaved Arrowwood (*Viburnum acerifolium*)
Matrimony-vine (*Lycium chinense*)
Mayflower (*Epigaea repens* var. *glabrifolia*)
Meadowsweet (*Spiraea latifolia*)
Mistletoe (*Arceuthobium pusillum*)
Mitchella repens L. (Partridge-berry), 6, Pl. LIX
Mooseberry (*Viburnum edule*)
Moosewood (*Acer pensylvanicum* or *Viburnum alnifolium*)
Morrow honeysuckle (*Lonicera morrowi*)
Moss-pink (*Phlox subulata*)
Mountain
    Bilberry (*Vaccinium uliginosum* var. *alpinum*)
    Cranberry (*V. vitis-idaea* var. *minus*)
    Fly Honeysuckle (*Lonicera villosa*)
    Heath (*Phyllodoce caerulea*)
    Holly (*Nemopanthus mucronata*)
    Juniper (*Juniperus communis* var. *saxatilis*)
    Paper Birch (*Betula papyrifera* var. *cordifolia*)
Mountain-ash
    American (*Pyrus americana* or *P. decora*)
    European (*P. aucuparia*)
Mountain-laurel (*Kalmia latifolia*)
Myrica, 7, 15, 17, 24, 25, Pl. XIV
    gale L. (Sweet Gale), 15, 25, Pl. XIV
    pensylvanica Loisel. (Bayberry), 7, 17, 24, Pl. XIV

Nanny-berry (*Viburnum lentago*)
Nemopanthus mucronata (L.) Trel. (Mountain Holly), 14, Pl. XXXVIII
New England Grape (*Vitis novae-angliae*)
New Jersey
    Tea (*Ceanothus americanus*)
    Blueberry (*Vaccinium caesariense*)
Nightshade
    Bitter (*Solanum dulcamara*)
    Climbing (*S. dulcamara*)
Nine-bark (*Physocarpus opulifolius*)

Northern
    Fox Grape (*Vitis labrusca*)
    Prickly-ash (*Zanthoxylum americanum*)
    Red-Oak (*Quercus rubra* var. *borealis*)
    White Pine (*Pinus strobus*)
    White-cedar (*Thuja occidentalis*)
Norway
    Maple (*Acer platanoides*)
    Pine (*Pinus resinosa*)
Nyssa sylvatica Marsh. (Black Tupelo, Black-gum), 13, Pl. XLVII

Oak (*Quercus*)
    Bear (*Q. ilicifolia*)
    Black (*Q. velutina*)
    Bur (*Q. macrocarpa*)
    Chestnut (*Q. prinus*)
    Northern Red (*Q. rubra* var. *borealis*)
    Poison- (*Rhus radicans*)
    Red (*Q. rubra*)
    Scarlet (*Q. coccinea*)
    Swamp White (*Q. bicolor*)
    White (*Q. alba*)
Old-field Birch (*Betula populifolia*)
Osier
    Purple (*Salix purpurea*)
Ostrya virginiana (Mill.) K. Koch (Eastern or American Hophornbeam, Ironwood, Leverwood), 15, 16, 19, Pl. XVIII

Pagoda Dogwood (*Cornus alternifolia*)
Pale-laurel (*Kalmia polifolia*)
Panicled Dogwood (*Cornus racemosa*)
Paper Birch (*Betula papryifera*)
    Dwarf (*B. minor*)
    Mountain (*B. papyrifera* var. *cordifolia*)
Parthenocissus (Virginia Creeper, Woodbine), 11, 25, Pl. XLII
    quinquefolia (L.) Planch. (Virginia Creeper, Woodbine), 25, Pl. XLII
    inserta (Kern.) K. Fritsch. (Virginia Creeper, Woodbine), 25, Pl. XLII
Partridge-berry (*Mitchella repens*)
Pepperbush
    Sweet (*Clethra alnifolia*)
Phlox subulata L. (Ground-or Moss-pink), 6, Pl. LIII
Phyllodoce caerulea (L.) Bab. (Mountain Heath), 7, Pl. LII
Physocarpus opulifolius (L.) Maxim. (Nine-bark), 18, Pl. XXVI
Picea (Spruce), 5, 25, Pl. III
    glauca (Moench) Voss. (White Spruce), 25, Pl. III
    mariana (Mill.) BSP. (Black Spruce), 25, Pl. III
    rubens Sarg. (Red Spruce), 25, Pl. III
Pilgrim Grape (*Vitis novae-angliae*)
Pimbina (*Viburnum edule*)

49

idaeus L. (Red Raspberry), 29, Pl. XXXII

occidentalis L. (Black Raspberry), 29, Pl. XXXII

odoratus L. (Purple Flowering Raspberry), 29, Pl. XXXII

pubescens Raf., 11, 29, Pl. XXXII

Rugosa rose (*Rosa rugosa*)

Rum Cherry (*Prunus serotina*)

Russet Buffalo-berry (*Shepherdia canadensis*)

Sage Willow (*Salix candida*)

Salix (Willow), 2, 9, 14, 30, 31, Pls. VIII-XIII

alba L. (White Willow), 31, 35, Pl. XII

alba L. X *fragilis* L., 35

arctophila Cockerell, 30, Pl. IX

argyrocarpa Anderss., 30, Pl. IX

bebbiana Sarg. (Bebb Willow), 31, Pl. XIII

candida Fluegge (Sage or Hoary Willow), 31, Pl. X

coactilis Fern., 30, Pl. XI

cordata Michx., 31, Pl. XI

var. *abrasa* Fern., 31

discolor Muhl. (Pussy or Glaucous Willow), 31, Pl. XIII

var. *latifolia* Anderss. (Silver Pussy Willow), 31

fragilis L. (Crack or Brittle Willow), 30, 35, Pl. XII

glaucophylloides Fern., 31, Pl. XIII

gracilis Anderss., 30, Pl. XI

herbacea L. (Dwarf Willow), 30, Pl. IX

humilis Marsh. (Prairie Willow), 31, Pl. XIII

interior Rowlee (Sandbar Willow), 30, Pl. X

lucida Muhl. (Shining Willow), 30, Pl. XII

var. *angustifolia* Anderss., 30, Pl. XII

var. *intonsa* Fern., 30, Pl. XII

nigra Marsh. (Black Willow), 30, Pl. XII

pedicellaris Pursh (Bog Willow), 30, Pl. X

pellita Anderss., 30, Pl. X

planifolia Pursh, 30, Pl. IX

purpurea L. (Purple Willow, Purple Osier), 9, 30, Pl. VIII

pyrifolia Anderss. (Balsam Willow), 31, Pl. XIII

rigida Muhl., 31, Pl. XI

f. *mollis* (Palmer & Steyerm.) Fern., 31

sericea Marsh. (Silky Willow), 30, Pl. XI

X *smithiana* Willd., 31, Pl. VIII

uva-ursi Pursh (Bearberry Willow), 30, Pl. IX

Sambucus (Elder), 10, 31, 35, Pl. LXI

canadensis L. (Common, American, or Black-berried Elder), 31, Pl. LXI

pubens Michx. (Red-berried Elder), 31, 35, Pl. LXI

f. *calva* Fern., 35

Sand Cherry (*Prunus depressa* or *P. susquehanae*)

Sandbar Willow (*Salix interior*)

Sarsaparilla (*Aralia*)

Bristly (*A. hispida*)

Prickly (*A. hispida*)

Wild (*A. nudicaulis*)

Sassafras albidum (Nutt.) Nees (Sassafras), 14, 17, 35, Pl. XXIV

var. *molle* (Raf.) Fern., 35

Sassafras (*Sassafras albidum*)

Scarlet Oak (*Quercus coccinea*)

Scotch Rose (*Rosa spinosissima*)

Serviceberry (*Amelanchier*)

Allegheny (*A. laevis*)

Downy (*A. arborea*)

Mountain (*A. bartramiana*)

Shad (*Amelanchier*)

Shad-bush (*Amelanchier*)

Shagbark Hickory (*Carya ovata*)

Sheep-laurel (*Kalmia angustifolia*)

Shepherdia canadensis (L.) Nutt. (Russet Buffalo-berry), 9, Pl. XLIV

Shining

Sumac (*Rhus copallina* var. *latifolia*)

Willow (*Salix lucida*)

Shrubby

Bittersweet (*Celastrus scandens*)

Cinquefoil (*Potentilla fruticosa*)

Silky

Cornel (*Cornus amomum* or *C. obliqua*)

Dogwood (*Cornus amomum* or *C. obliqua*)

Willow (*Salix sericea*)

Silver

Maple (*Acer saccharinum*)

Pussy Willow (*Salix discolor* var. *latifolia*)

Skunk Currant (*Ribes glandulosum*)

Slippery Elm (*Ulmus rubra*)

Small Cranberry (*Vaccinium oxycoccos*)

Small-tooth Aspen (*Populus tremuloides*)

Smilax rotundifolia L. (Common Greenbrier), 11, Pl. VI

Smooth

Alder (*Alnus serrulata*)

Gooseberry (*Ribes hirtellum*)

Sumac (*Rhus glabra*)

Winterberry (*Ilex laevigata*)

Snowberry (*Symphoricarpos albus* var. *laevigatus*)

Creeping (*Gaultheria hispidula*)

Solanum dulcamara L. (Climbing or Bitter Nightshade, European Bittersweet), 11, 35, Pl. LVIII

Sorbaria sorbifolia (L.) A. Br. (Ural False-spiraea), 16, 18, Pl. XXXIII

Sour-top Blueberry (*Vaccinium myrtilloides*)

Speckled Alder (*Alnus rugosa*)

Spice-bush (*Lindera benzoin*)

Spiraea (Spiraea), 14, 31, 35, Pl. XXXIII

latifolia (Ait.) Borkh. (Meadowseet), 31, 35, Pl. XXXIII

var. *septentrionalis* Fern., 35

tomentosa L. (Hardhack, Steeple Bush), 31, Pl. XXXIII

Spiraea

Ural False- (*Sorbaria sorbifolia*)

Spruce

Black (*Picea mariana*)

Red (*P. rubens*)

50

White (*P. glauca*)
Squashberry (*Viburnum edule*)
Staghorn Sumac (*Rhus. typhina*)
Steeple Bush (*Spiraea tomentosa*)
Striped Maple (*Acer pensylvanicum*)
Sugar Maple (*Acer saccharum*)
Sumac
    Dwarf (*Rhus copallina* var. *latifolia*)
    Poison (*R. vernix*)
    Shining (*R. copallina* var. *latifolia*)
    Smooth (*R. glabra*)
    Staghorn (*R. typhina*)
Swamp
    Birch (*Betula pumila*)
    Black Currant (*Ribes lacustre*)
    Blueberry (*Vaccinium corymbosum*)
    Dewberry (*Rubus hispidus*)
    Fly Honeysuckle (*Lonicera oblongifolia*)
    Red Currant (*Ribes triste*)
    White Oak (*Quercus bicolor*)
Sweet
    Birch (*Betula lenta*)
    Gale (*Myrica gale*)
    Pepperbush (*Clethra alnifolia*)
    Viburnum (*Viburnum lentago*)
Sweet-brier (*Rosa eglanteria*)
Sweet-fern (*Comptonia peregrina*)
Sycamore (*Platanus occidentalis*)
    American (*P. occidentalis*)
Symphoricarpos albus (L.) Blake var. *laevigatus* (Fern.) Blake (Snowberry), 9, Pl. LXII
Syringa vulgaris L. (Common Lilac), 10, Pl. LVII

Tamarack (*Larix laricina*)
Tartarian Honeysuckle (*Lonicera tatarica*)
Taxus candensis Marsh. (American Yew, Ground-hemlock), 5, Pl. I
Tea
    Labrador (*Ledum groenlandicum*)
    New Jersey (*Ceanothus americanus*)
Teaberry (*Gaultheria procumbens*)
Thorn-apple (*Crataegus*)
Three-toothed Cinquefoil (*Potentilla tridentata*)
Thuja occidentalis L. (Northern White-cedar, Eastern Arbor-vitae), 5, Pl. II
Thyme
    Creeping (*Thymus serpyllum*)
Thymus serpyllum L. (Creeping Thyme), 2
Tilia americana L. (American Basswood, American Linden), 16, Pl. XLIV
Tootheache-tree (*Zanthoxylum americanum*)
Trailing Arbutus (*Epigaea repens* var. *glabrifolia*)
Tree
    Rowan (*Pyrus aucuparia*)
    Toothache (*Zanthoxylum · americanum*)
Trembling Aspen (*Populus tremuloides*)

Trumpet Honeysuckle (*Lonicera sempervirens*)
Tsuga canadensis (L.) Carr. (Eastern Hemlock), 5, Pl. I
Tupelo
    Black (*Nyssa sylvatica*)
Twin-flower (*Linnaea borealis* var. *americana*)

Ulmus (Elm), 16, 19, Pl. XIX
    americana L. (American or White Elm), 16, 19, Pl. XIX
    rubra Muhl. (Slippery or Red Elm), 19
Ural False-spiraea (*Sorbaria sorbifolia*)

Vaccinium (Bilberry, Blueberry, Cranberry), 2, 8, 15, 32, 35, Pls. LIV-LVI
    angustifolium Ait. (Low Sweet or Late Sweet Blueberry), 32, 35
        var. *laevifolium* House, 32, 35, Pl. LVI
    atrococcum (Gray) Heller (Black Highbush or Downy Swamp Blueberry), 32, Pl. LV
    caesariense Mackenz. (New Jersey Blueberry), 32, Pl. LV
    cespitosum Michx. (Dwarf Bilberry), 15, 32, Pl. LVI
    corymbosum L. (Highbush or Swamp Blueberry), 32, Pl. LV
    macrocarpon Ait. (Large or American Cranberry), 32, Pl. LIV
    myrtilloides Michx. (Canada, Sour-top or Velvet-leaf Blueberry), 32, Pl. LVI
    oxycoccos L. (Small Cranberry), 32, 35, Pl. LIV
        var. *ovalifolium* Michx., 35
    uliginosum L. var. *alpinum* Bigel. (Bog or Mountain Bilberry), 15, 32, Pl. LVI
    vitis-idaea L. var. *minus* Lodd. (Mountain or Rock Cranberry), 8, 32, Pl. LIV
Velvet-leaf Blueberry (*Vaccinium myrtilloides*)
Veronica officinalis L. (Common Speedwell), 2
Viburnum (Arrow-wood), 9, 10, 32, 33, Pls. LXII & LXIII
    acerifolium L. (Maple-leaved Arrow-wood, Dockmackie), 33, Pl. LXII
    alnifolium Marsh. (Hobble-bush, Witch Hobble, Moosewood), 9, 32, Pl. LXII
    cassinoides L. (Withe-rod, Wild Raisin), 33, Pl. LXIII
    edule (Mich.) Raf. (Squashberry, Mooseberry, Pimbina), 32, Pl. LXIII
    lentago L. (Nanny-berry, Sweet Viburnum, Wild Raisin), 32, Pl. LXIII
    recognitum Fern., (Arrow-wood), 33, Pl. LXII
    trilobum Marsh. (Highbush Cranberry), 32, Pl. LXIII
Viburnum
    Sweet (*Viburnum lentago*)
Vinca minor L. (Periwinkle), 2
Vine
    Common Matrimony- (*Lycium chinense*)
Virginia Creeper (*Parthenocissus inserta* or *P. quinquefolia*)

51

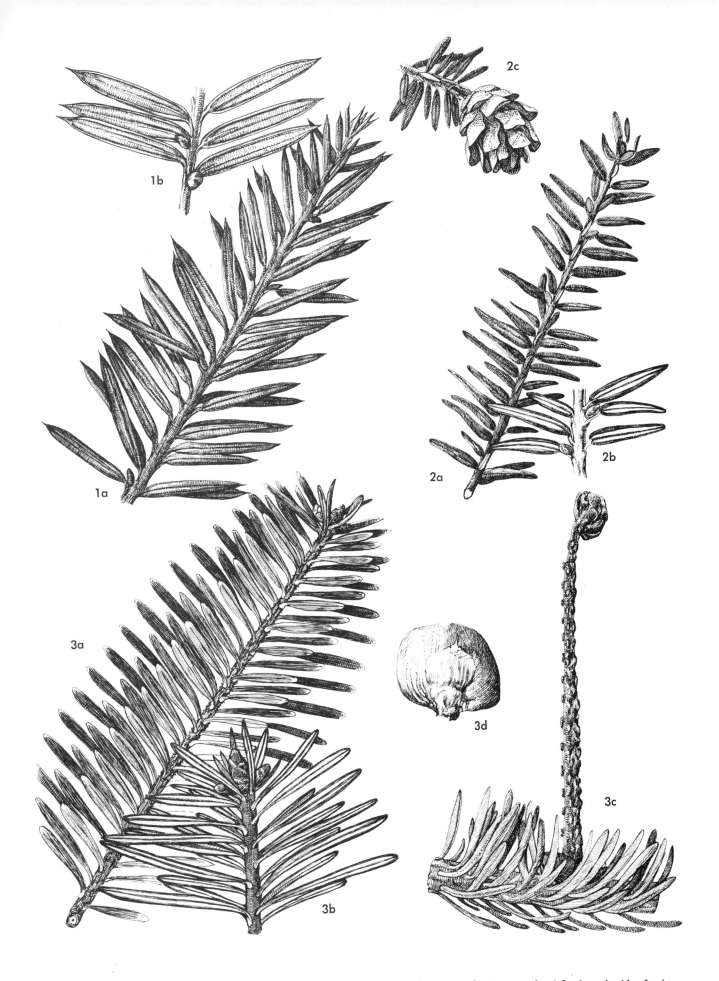

Plate I. 1. *Taxus canadensis:* **a,** twig x1.5; **b,** underside of twig x2.3. **2.** *Tsuga canadensis:* **a,** twig x1.5; **b,** underside of twig x2.3; **c,** fruiting branch and cone x1.5; **3.** *Abies balsamea:* **a,** twig x1.5; **b,** underside of tip of twig x1.9; **c.** fruiting branch and naked cone axis x1.5; **d,** cone scale and subtending bract x3.

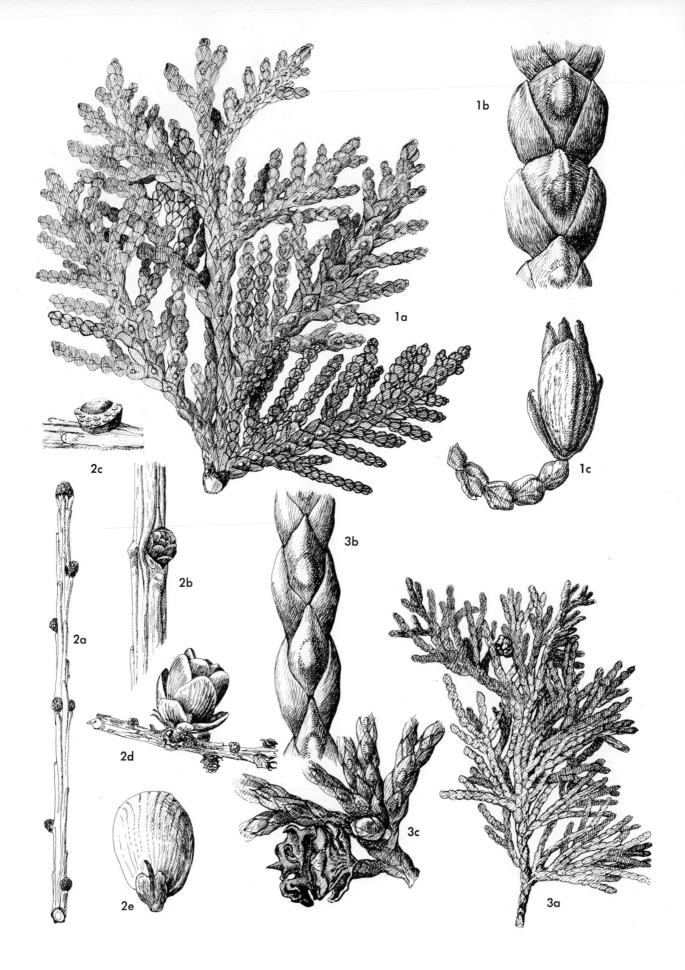

Plate II. **1.** *Thuja occidentalis:* **a,** tip of branch x1.5; **b,** twig, dorsal view x12; **c,** cone x3.7. **2.** *Larix laricina;* **a,** twig x1.5; **b,** node x3; **c,** spur shoot x4.5; **d,** fruiting branch and cone x1.5; **e,** cone scale and subtending bract x3. **3.** *Chamaecyparis thyoides:* **a,** tip of branch x1.5; **b,** twig, dorsal view x15; **c,** fruiting branch and cone x3.

Plate III. 1. *Picea glauca:* **a,** twig x1.5; **b,** underside of twig x2.7; **c,** cone x¾; **d,** cone scale x1.5; **e,** cross-section of needle x15. **2.** *P. rubens:* **a,** twig x1.5; **b,** underside of twig x3; **c,** cone x¾; **d,** base of cone x¾; **e,** cone scale x1.5; **f,** cross-section of needle x15. **3.** *P. mariana:* **a,** twig x1.5; **b,** underside of twig x3: **c,** cone x¾; **d,** base of cone x¾; **e,** cone scale x1.5; **f,** cross-section of needle x15.

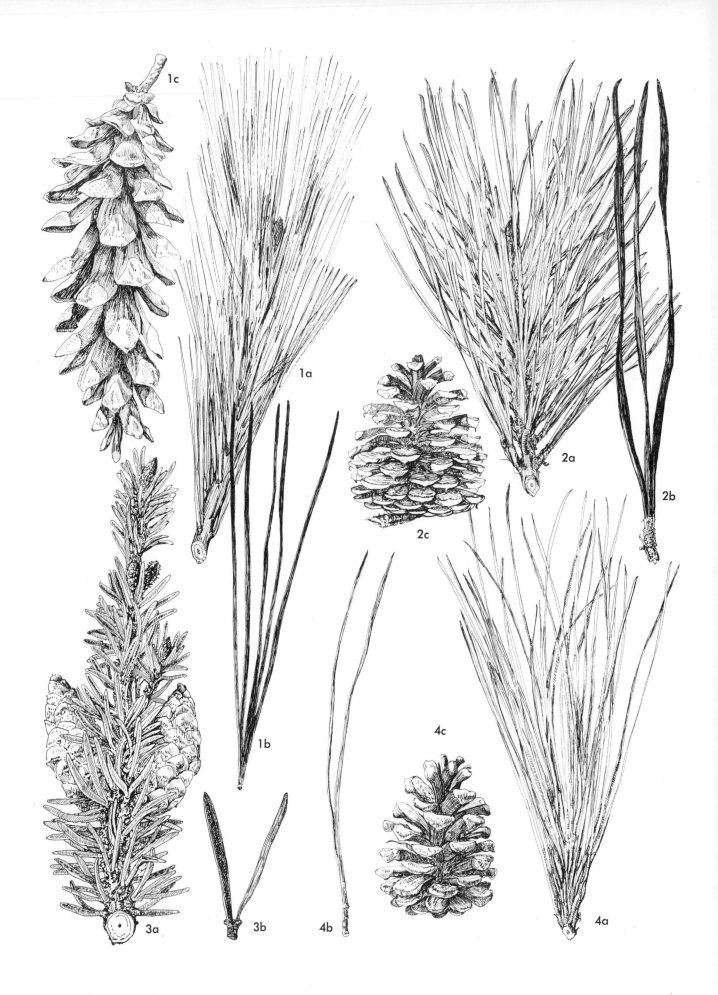

Plate IV. **1.** *Pinus strobus:* **a,** twig x¾; **b,** fascicle x1.5; **c,** cone x¾. **2.** *P. rigida:* **a,** twig x¾; **b,** fascicle x1.5; **c,** cone x¾. **3.** *P. banksiana:* **a,** twig with cones x¾; **b,** fascicle x1.5. **4.** *P. resinosa:* **a,** twig x¾; **b,** fascicle x1.5; **c,** cone x¾.

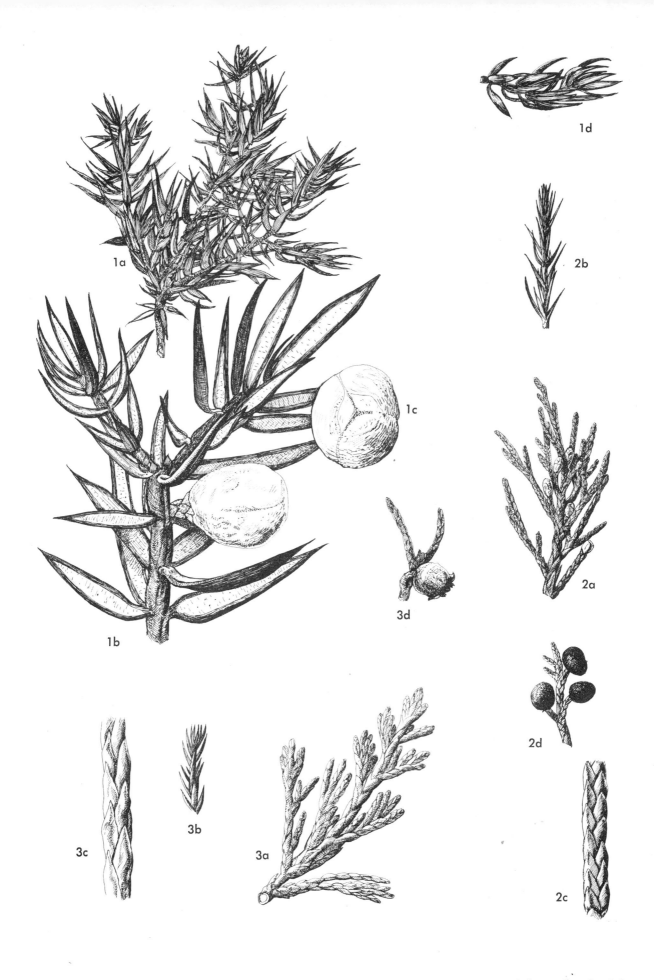

Plate V. **1.** *Juniperus communis* var. *depressa:* **a,** tip of branch x1.5; **b,** tip of fruiting branch x4.5; **c,** fruit, top view x5; **d,** *J. c.* var. *saxatalis:* twig x1.5. **2.** *J. virginiana* var. *crebra:* **a,** tip of branch x1.5; **b,** juvenile foliage x1.5; **c,** mature foliage x6; **d,** fruiting branch x1.5. **3.** *horizontalis:* **a,** tip of branch x1.5; **b,** juvenile foliage x1.5; **c,** mature foliage x6; **d,** fruiting branch x1.5.

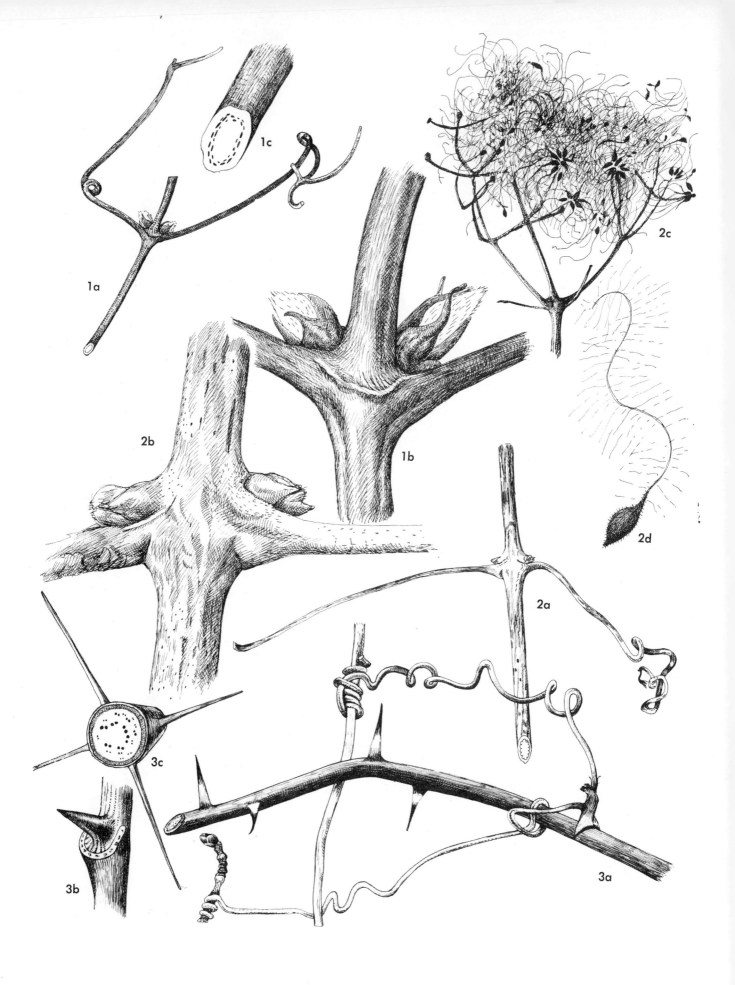

Plate VI. 1. *Clematis verticillaris:* **a,** twig x¾; **b,** node x4.5; **c,** pith x5.5. **2.** *C. virginiana:* **a,** twig x¾; **b,** node x4.5; **c,** inflorescence x¾; **d,** fruit x4.5. **3.** *Smilax rotundifolia:* **a,** twig x1.5; **b,** node (petiole base removed) x4.5; , pith x5.5.

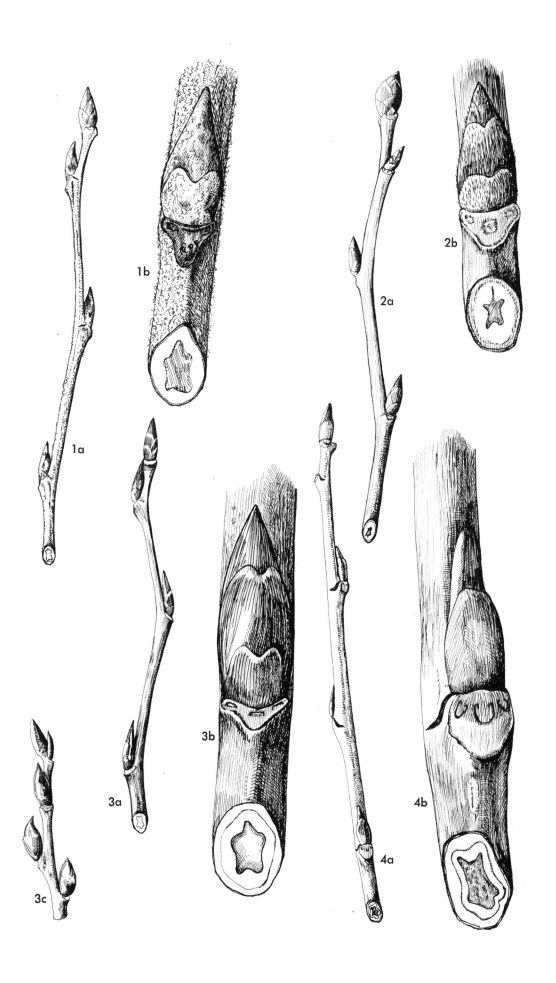

Plate VII. **1.** *Populus alba:* **a,** twig x1.5; **b,** node x5.5. **2.** *P. grandidentata:* **a,** twig x1.5; **b,** node x5.5. **3.** *P. tremuloides:* **a,** twig x1.5; **b,** node x7.5; **c,** tip of twig showing floral and vegetative buds x1.5. **4.** *P. nigra:* **a,** twig x1.5; **b,** node x7.5.

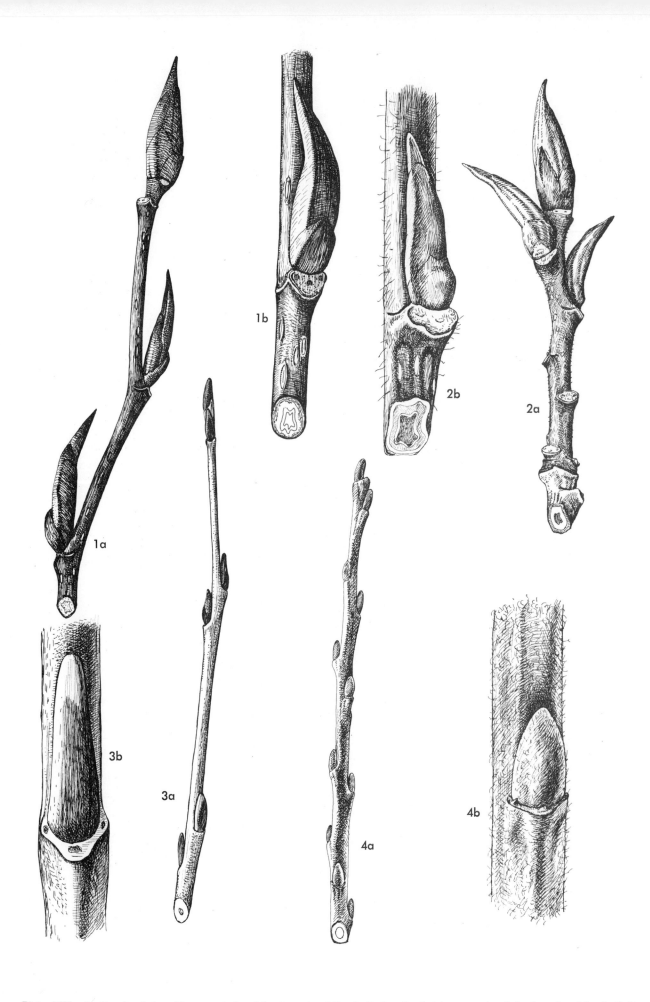

Plate VIII. **1.** *Populus balsamifera:* **a,** twig x1.5; **b,** node x2.3. **2.** X *P. gileadensis:* **a,** twig x1.5; **b** node x4.5. **3.** *Salix purpurea:* **a,** twig x1.5; **b,** node x6.7. **4.** X *S. smithiana:* **a,** twig x1.5; **b,** node x6.

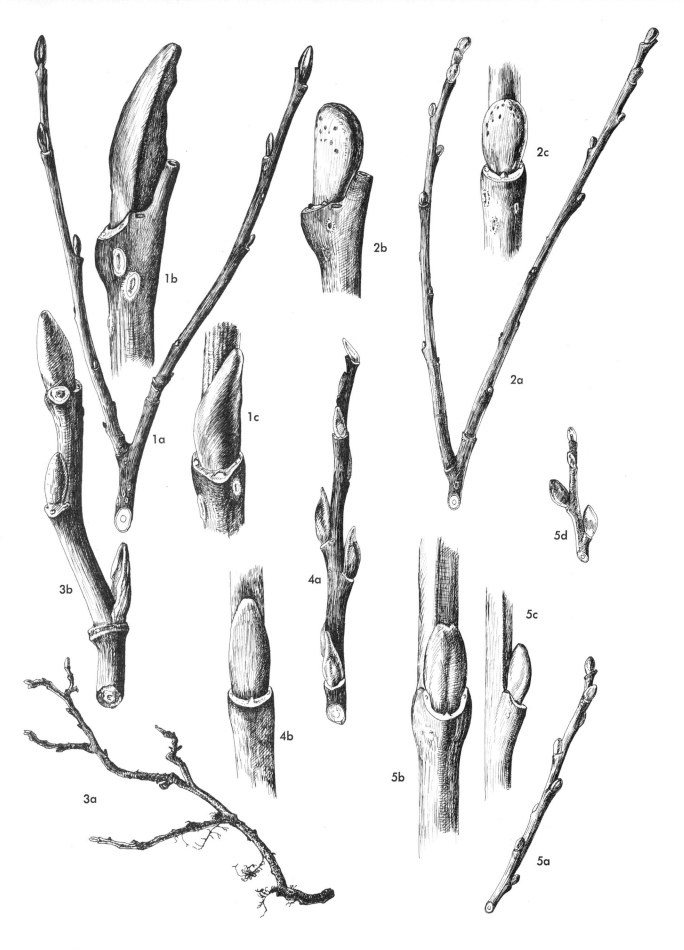

Plate IX. 1. *Salix arctophila:* **a,** branch x1.5; **b,** pseudoterminal bud x8; **c,** node x5.5. **2.** *S. argyrocarpa:* **a,** branch x1.5; **b,** pseudoterminal bud x8; **c,** node x6. **3.** *S. herbacea:* **a,** entire plant, showing subterranean portion with roots at nodes and aerial portion x1.5; **b,** twig (showing empty pseudoterminal bud scale from previous season) x9. **4.** *S. planifolia:* **a,** twig x1.5; **b,** node x 6.7. **5.** *S. uva-ursi:* **a,** twig x1.5; **b,** node, face view x9; **c,** node, lateral view x6; **d,** tip of twig showing floral and vegetative buds x1.5.

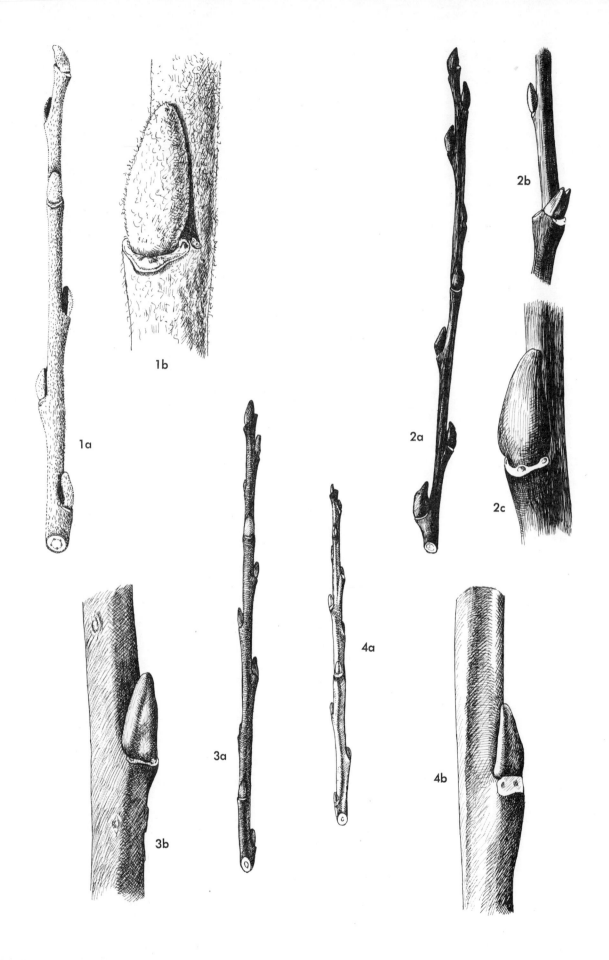

Plate X. 1. *Salix candida:* **a,** twig x1.5; **b,** node x6. **2.** *S. pedicellaris:* **a,** twig x1.5; **b,** base of twig showing empty pseudoterminal bud scale from previous season x2.3; **c,** node x6. **3.** *S. pellita:* **a,** twig x1.5; **b,** node x6. **4.** *S. interior:* **a,** twig x1.5; **b,** node x6.

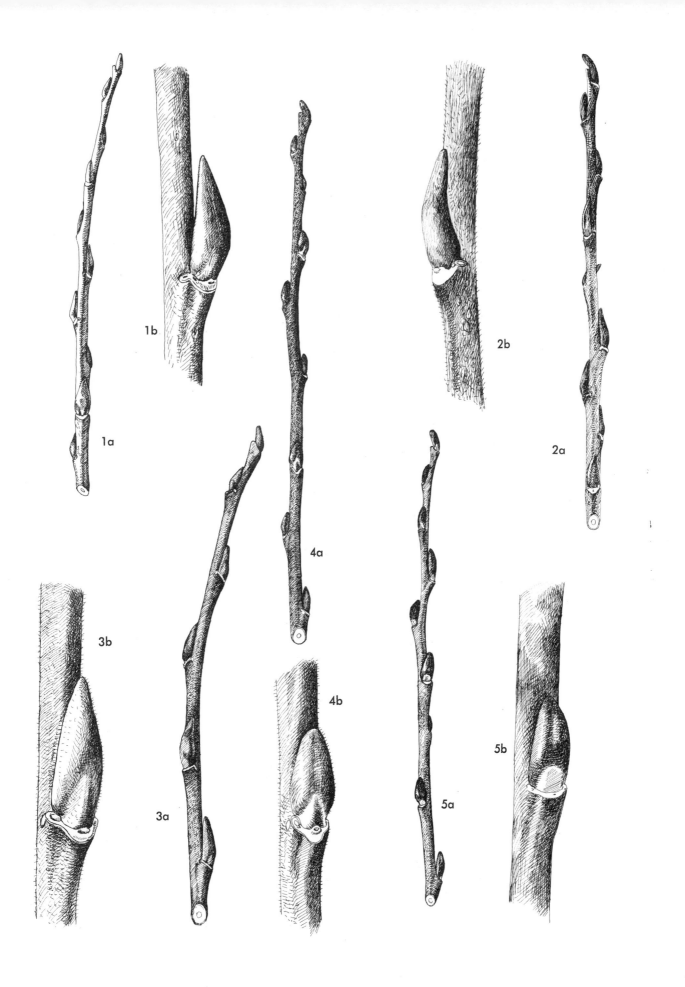

Plate XI. **1.** *Salix rigida:* **a,** twig x1.5; **b,** node x4.5. **2.** *S. cordata:* **a,** twig x1.5; **b,** node x4.5. **3.** *S. coactilis:* **a,** twig x1.5; **b,** node x4.5. **4.** *S. sericea:* **a,** twig x1.5; **b,** node x4.5. **5.** *S. gracilis:* **a,** twig x1.5; **b,** node x4.5.

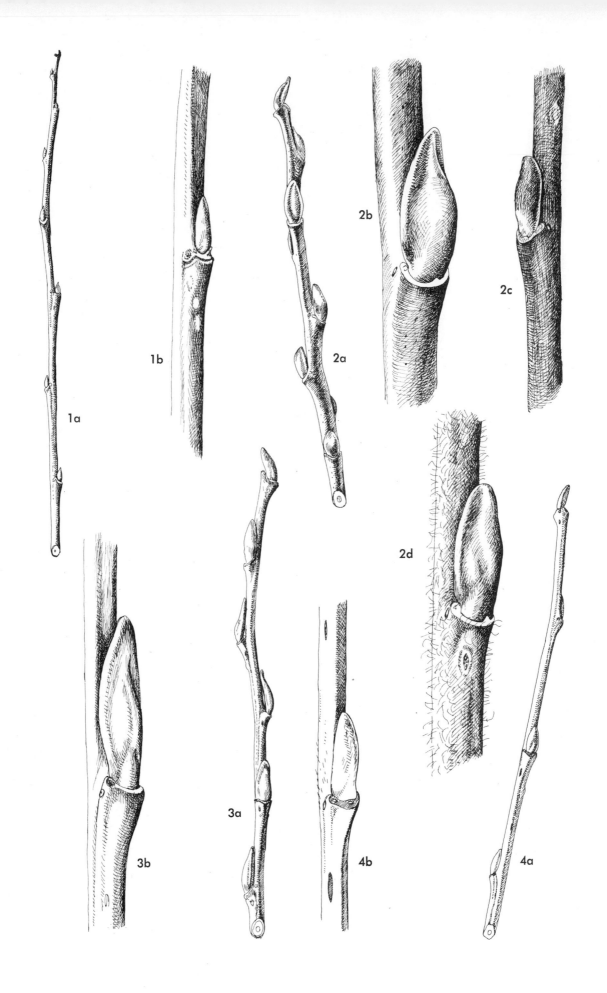

Plate XII. **1.** *Salix nigra:* **a,** twig x1.5; **b,** node x4.5. **2.** *S. lucida:* **a,** twig x1.5; **b,** node x4.5; **c,** *S. l.* var. *angustifolia:* node x4.5; **d,** *S. l.* var. *intonsa:* node x4.5. **3.** *S. fragilis:* **a,** twig x1.5; **b,** node x4.5. **4.** *S. alba:* **a,** twig x1.5; **b,** node x4.5.

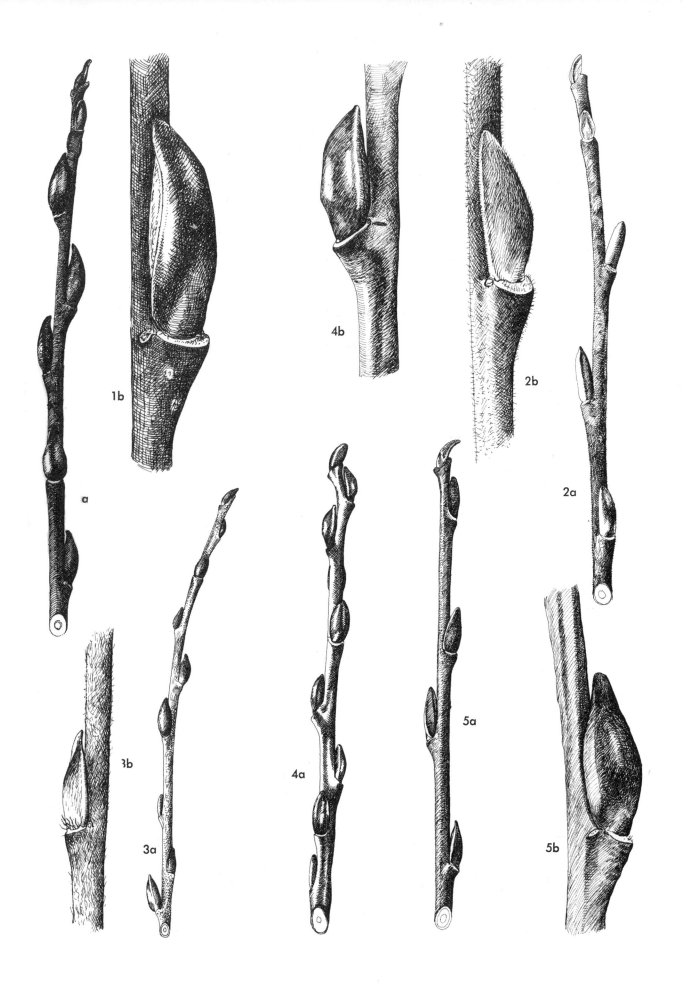

Plate XIII. **1.** *Salix discolor:* **a,** twig x1.5; **b,** node x4.5. **2.** *S. humilis:* **a,** twig x1.5; **b,** node x4.5. **3.** *S. bebbiana:* **a,** twig x1.5; **b,** node x4.5. **4.** *S. pyrifolia:* **a,** twig x1.5; **b,** node x4.5. **5.** *S. glaucophylloides:* **a,** twig x1.5; **b,** node x4.5.

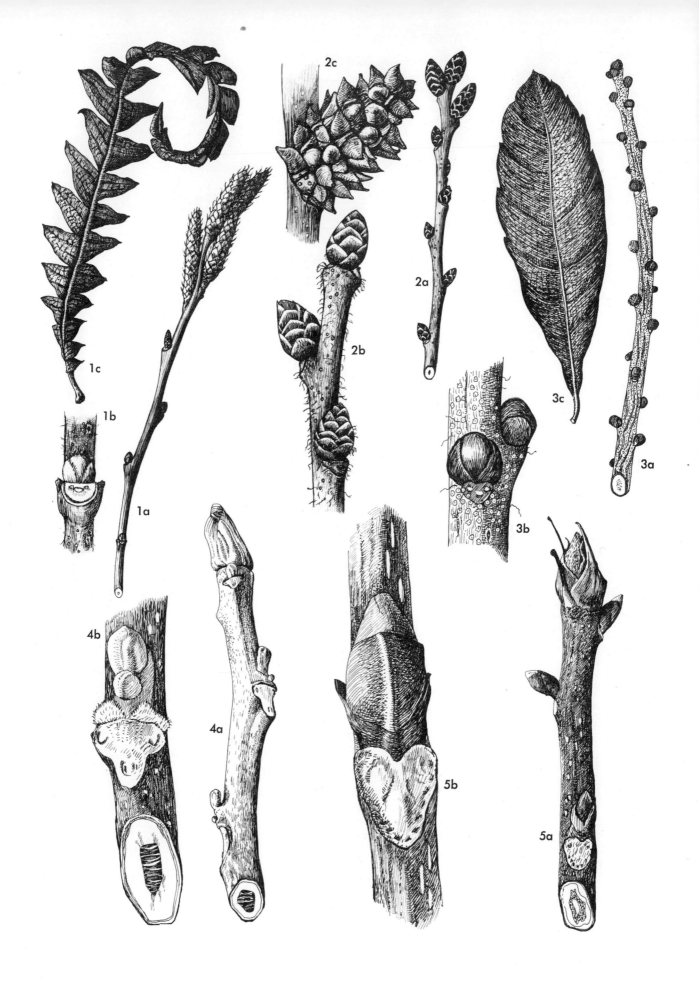

Plate XIV. **1.** *Comptonia peregrina:* **a,** twig with apical preformed staminate catkins x1.5; **b,** node x5; **c,** leaf x¾. **2.** *Myrica gale:* **a,** twig with apical preformed staminate catkins x1.5; **b,** tip of twig x9; **c,** fruit x3.7. **3.** *M. pensylvanica:* **a,** twig x1.5; **b,** nodes x7.5; **c,** leaf x1.5. **4.** *Juglans cinerea:* **a,** twig x1.5; **b,** node and pith x2.3. **5.** *Carya ovata:* **a,** twig x1.5; **b,** node x4.5.

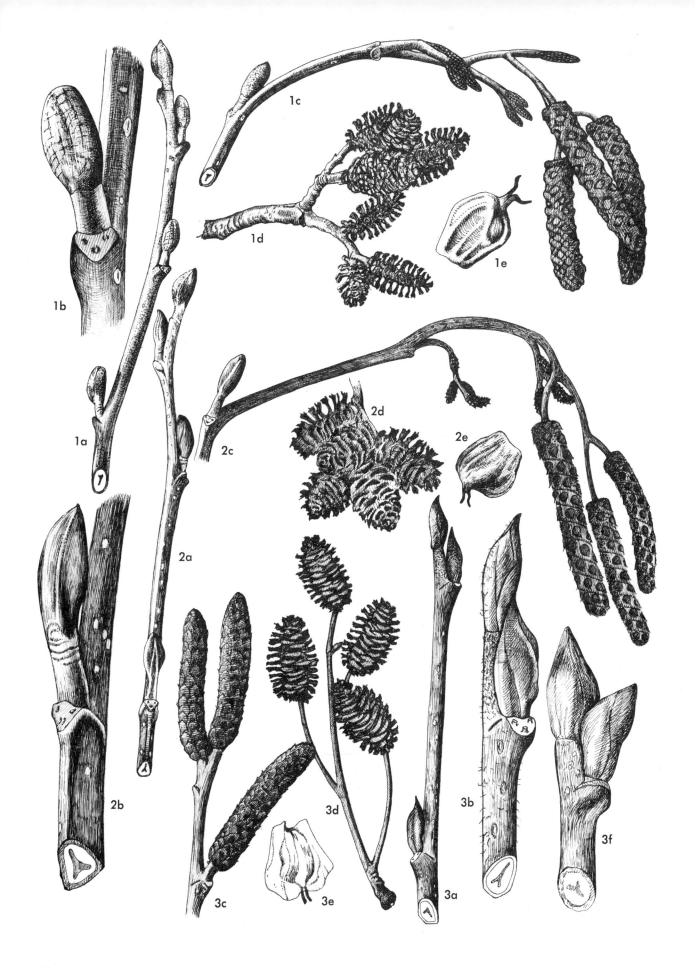

Plate XV. 1. *Alnus serrulata:* **a,** twig x1.5; **b,** node x4.5; **c,** tip of fertile twig with preformed pistillate and staminate (larger) catkins x1.5; **d,** strobili x1.5; **e,** nutlet x9. **2.** *Alnus rugosa:* **a,** twig x1.5; **b,** node x3.7; **c,** tip of fertile twig x1.5; **d,** strobili x1.5; **e,** nutlet x6. **3.** *Alnus crispa* var. *mollis:* **a,** twig x1.5; **b,** tip of twig x3; **c,** tip of fertile twig with preformed staminate catkins x1.5; **d,** strobili x1.5; **e,** nutlet x6; **f,** *A.c.* var. *crispa,* tip of twig x3.

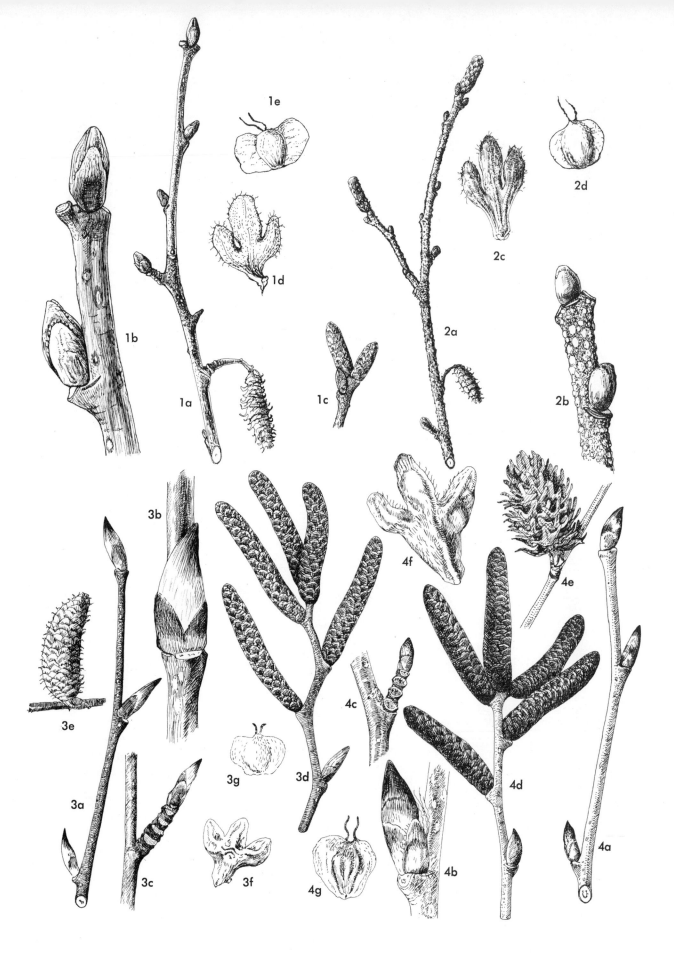

Plate XVI. **1.** *Betula minor:* **a,** twig and strobilus x1.5; **b,** tip of twig x5.5; **c,** tip of fertile twig with preformed staminate catkins x1.5; **d,** ovuliferous bract x4.5; **e,** nutlet x4.5. **2.** *B. glandulosa:* **a,** branch with strobilus and apical preformed staminate catkins x1.5; **b,** tip of twig x4.7; **c,** ovuliferous bract x3.7; **d,** nutlet x3.7. **3.** *B. lenta;* **a,** twig x1.5; **b,** node x5.3; **c,** spur shoot x1.5; **d,** preformed staminate catkins x1.5; **e,** strobilus x1.5; **f,** ovuliferous bract x3.7; **g,** nutlet x3.7. **4.** *B. lutea:* **a,** twig x1.5; **b,** node x3.7; **c,** spur shoot x1.5; **d,** preformed staminate catkins x1.5; **e,** strobilus x1.5; **f,** ovuliferous bract x3.7; **g,** nutlet x3.7.

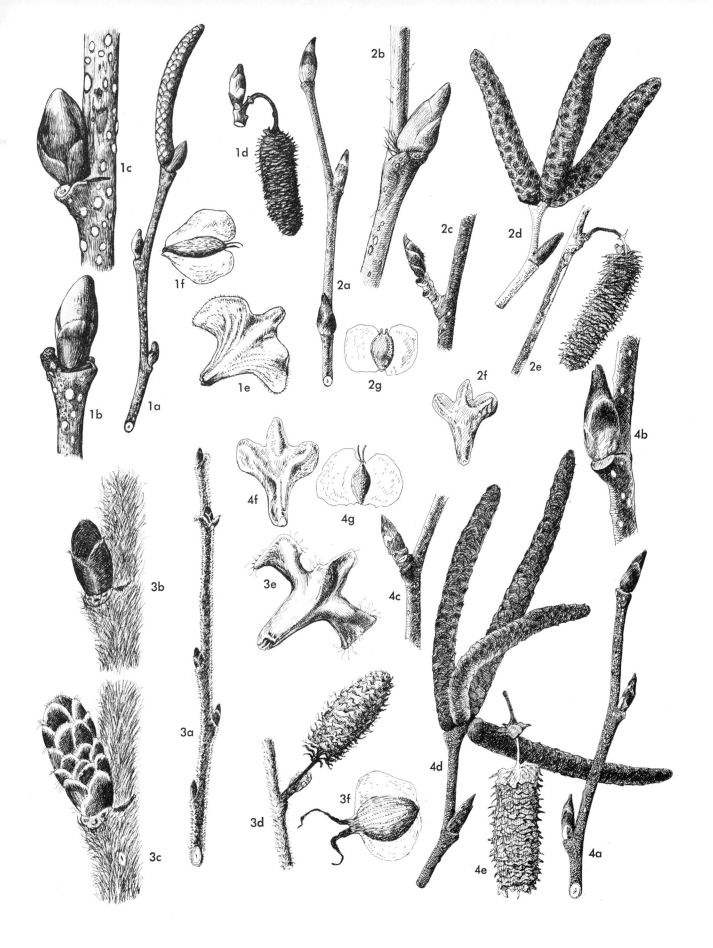

Plate XVII. **1.** *Betula populifolia:* **a,** twig with apical preformed staminate catkins x1.5; **b,** pseudoterminal bud x7; **c,** node x6; **d,** stobilus x1.5; **e,** ovuliferous bract x9; **f,** nutlet x7.5. **2.** *B. papyrifera:* **a,** twig x1.5; **b,** node x3; **c,** spur shoot x1.5; **d,** preformed staminate catkins x1.5; **e,** strobilus x1.5; **f,** ovuliferous bract x4.5; **g,** nutlet x4.5. **3.** *B. pumila:* **a,** twig x1.5; **b,** node x6; **c,** preformed staminate catkin x6; **d,** strobilus x1.5; **e,** ovuliferous bract x6.5; **f,** nutlet x6.5. **4.** *B. caerulea-grandis:* **a,** twig x1.5; **b,** node x3; **c,** spur shoot x1.5; **d,** preformed staminate catkins x1.5; **e,** strobilus x1.5; **f,** ovuliferous bract x4.5; **g,** nutlet x4.5.

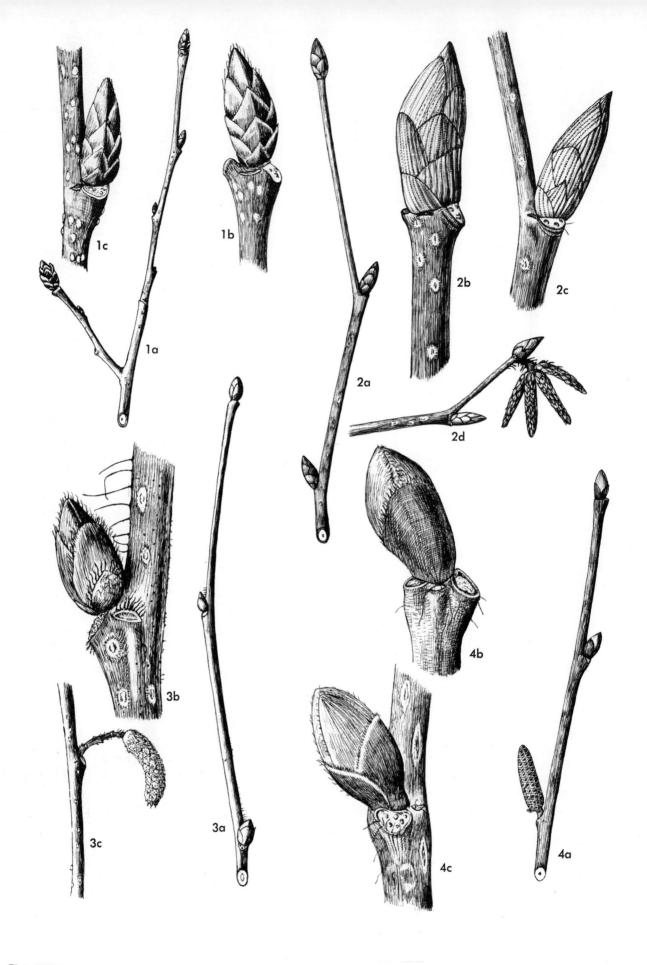

Plate XVIII. **1.** *Carpinus caroliniana* var. *virginiana:* **a,** branchlet and twig x1.5; **b,** pseudoterminal bud x6; **c,** node x6. **2.** *Ostrya virginiana:* **a,** twig x1.5; **b,** pseudoterminal bud x6; **c,** node x6; **d,** twig with preformed staminate catkins x1.5. **3.** *Corylus americana:* **a,** twig x1.5; **b,** node x7.5; **c,** preformed staminate catkin x1.5. **4.** *C. cornuta:* **a,** twig with preformed staminate catkin x1.5; **b,** pseudoterminal bud x7; **c,** node x6.

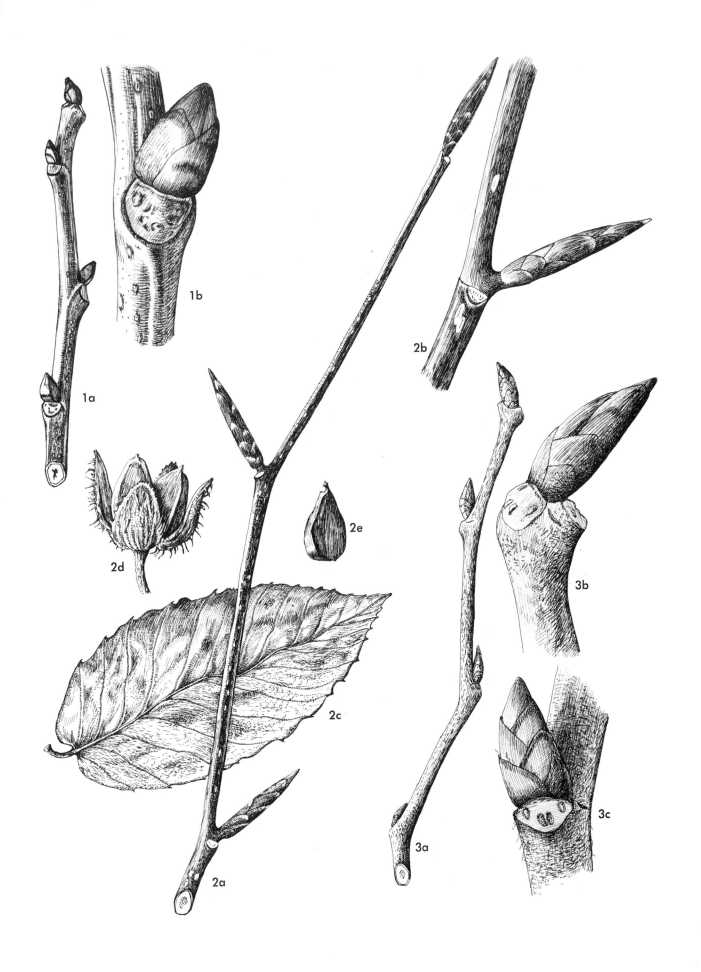

Plate XIX. **1.** *Castanea dentata:* **a,** twig x1.5; **b,** node x6. **2.** *Fagus grandifolia:* **a,** twig x1.5; **b,** node x2.3; **c,** leaf x¾; **d,** burr x1.5; **e,** nut x1.5. **3.** *Ulmus americana:* **a,** twig x1.5; **b,** pseudoterminal bud x6; **c,** node x6.

Plate XX. **1.** *Quercus alba:* **a,** twig x1.5; **b,** node x6; **c,** leaf x¾. **2.** *Q. prinus:* **a,** twig x1.5; **b,** node x3; **c,** leaf x¾. **3.** *Q. bicolor:* **a,** twig x1.5; **b,** tip of twig x3; **c,** leaf x3/4. **4.** *Q. macrocarpa:* **a,** twig x1.5; **b,** tip of twig x3; **c,** corky older branchlet x1.5; **d,** leaf x¾.

Plate XXI. **1.** *Quercus velutina:* **a,** twig x1.5; **b,** node x3; **c,** first-year acorn x2.3; **d,** leaf x¾. **2.** *Q. rubra:* **a,** twig x1.5; **b,** node x3; **c,** first-year acorn x2.3; **d,** leaf x¾. **3.** *Q. ilicifolia:* **a,** twig x1.5; **b,** node x6; **c,** first-year acorn x2.3; **d,** leaf x¾. **4.** *Q. coccinea:* **a,** twig x1.5; **b,** node x6; **c,** first-year acorn x2.3; **d,** leaf x¾.

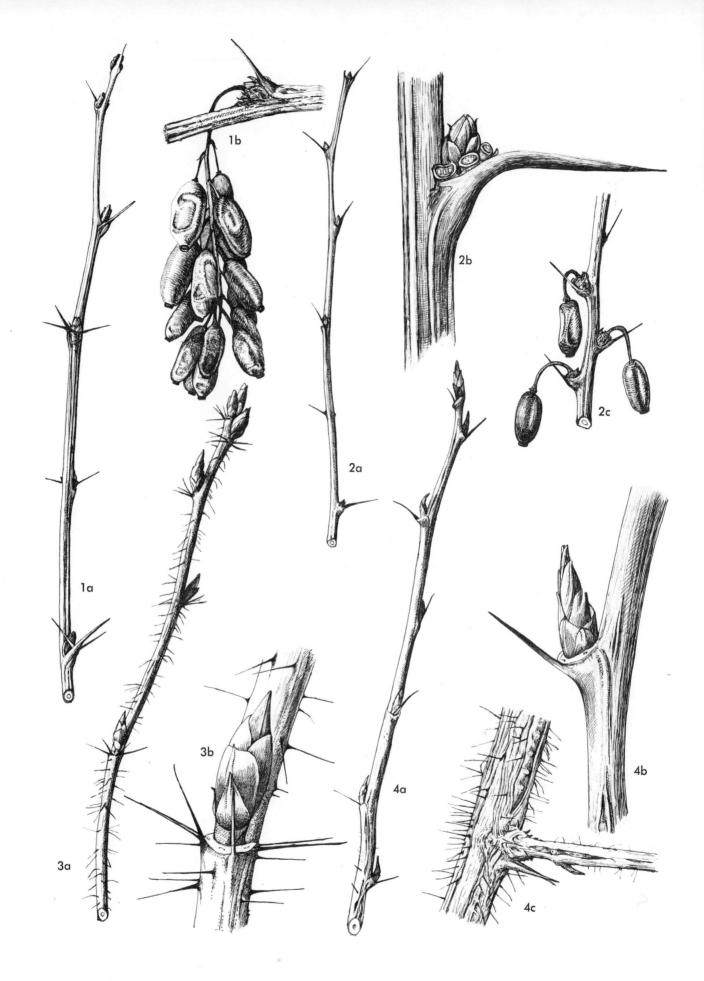

Plate XXII. **1.** *Berberis vulgaris:* **a,** twig x1.5. **b,** fruit x1.5. **2.** *B. thunbergii:* **a,** twig x1.5; **b,** node x6; **c,** fruit x1.5. **3.** *Ribes lacustre:* **a,** twig x1.5; **b,** node x6. **4.** *R. cynosbati:* **a,** twig x1.5; **b,** node x6; **c,** lower portion of stem and lateral branch x¾.

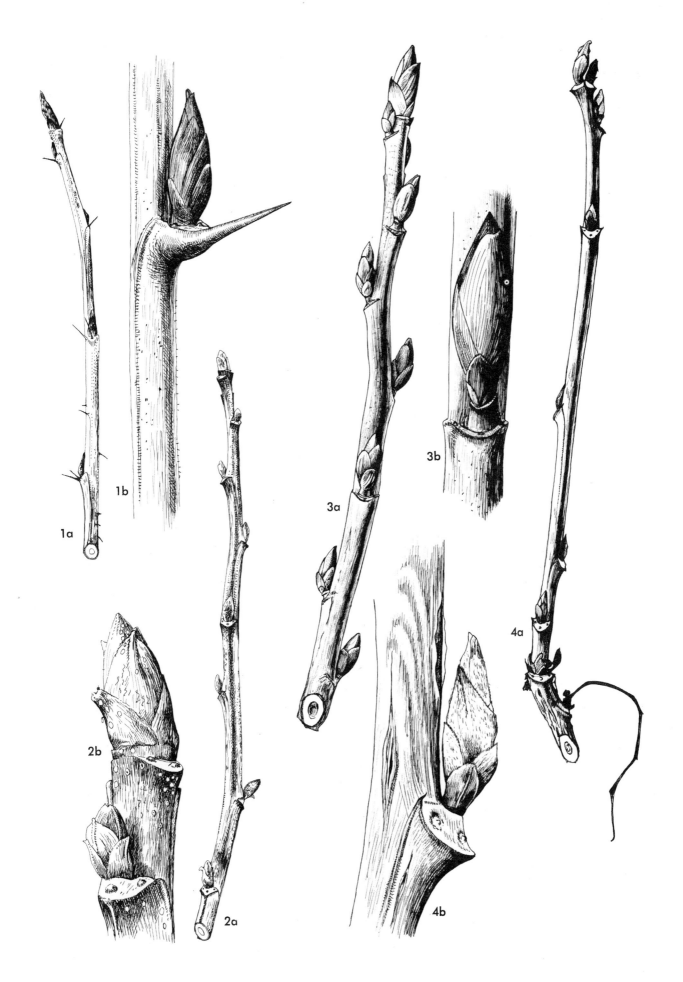

Plate XXIII. 1. *Ribes hirtellum:* **a**, twig x1.5; **b**, node x7.5. **2.** *R. americanum:* **a**, twig x1.5; **b**, node x7.5. **3.** *R. glandulosum:* **a**, twig x1.5; **b**, node x4.5. **4.** *R. triste:* **a**, twig x1.5; **b**, node x7.5.

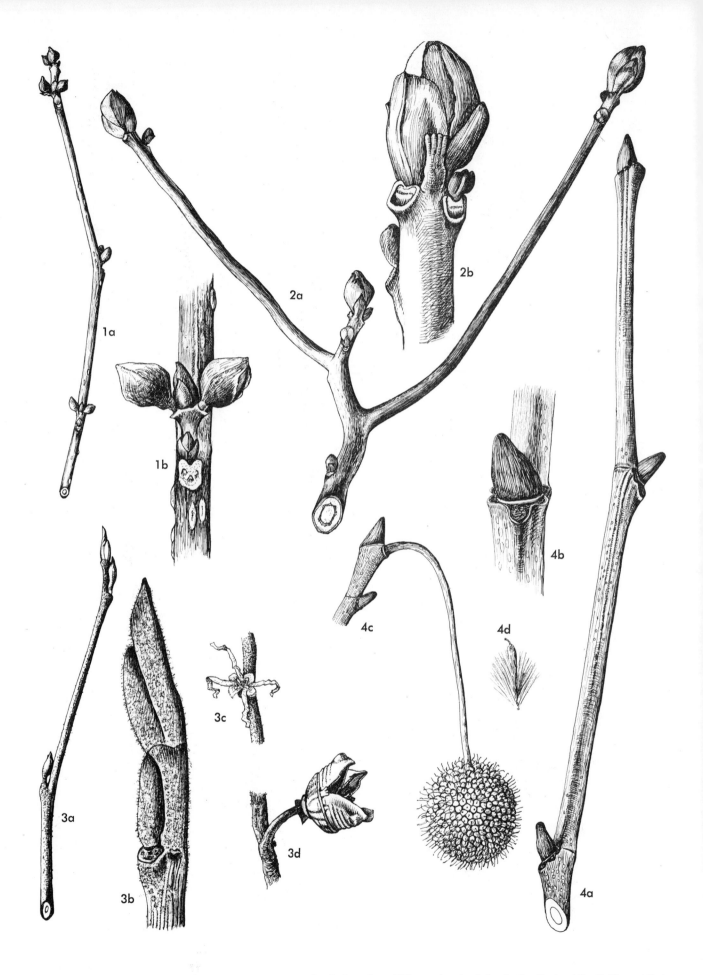

Plate XXIV. **1.** *Lindera benzoin:* **a,** twig x1.5; **b,** node x 6. **2.** *Sassafras albidum:* **a,** twig x1.5; **b,** tip of twig x4.5. **3.** *Hamamelis virginiana:* **a,** twig x1.5; **b,** tip of twig x4.5; **c,** flower x1.5; **d,** fruit x1.5. **4.** *Platanus occidentalis:* **a,** twig x1.5; **b,** node x3; **c,** fruiting head x¾; **d,** fruit x1.8.

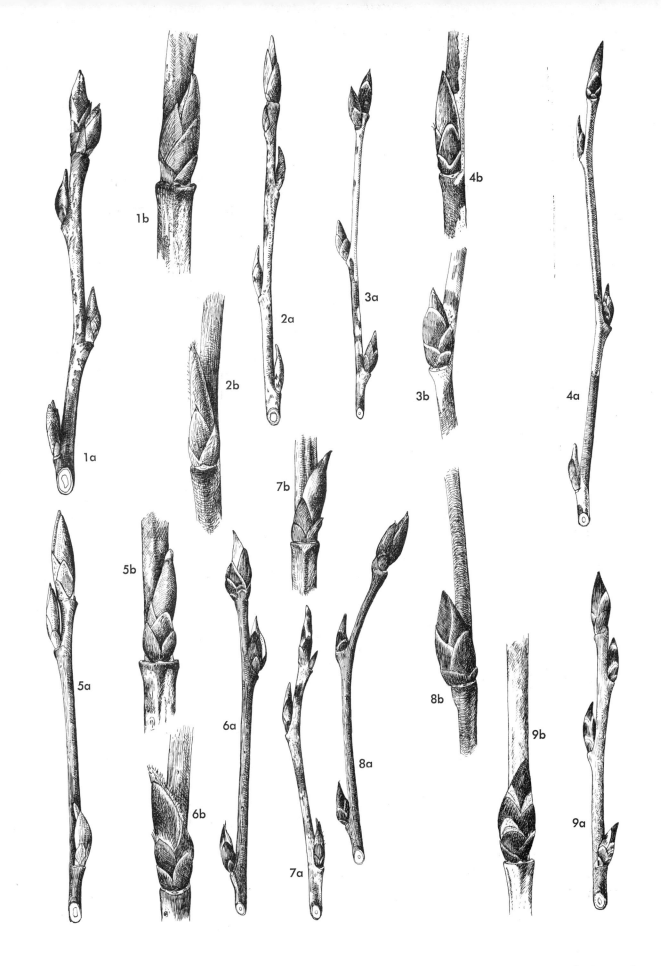

Plate XXV. 1. *Amelanchier laevis:* **a,** twig x1.5; **b,** node x3. **2.** *A. arborea:* **a,** twig x1.5; **b,** node x3. **3.** *A. canadensis:* **a,** twig x1.5; **b,** node x3. **4.** *A. intermedia:* **a,** twig x1.5; **b,** node x3. **5.** *A. wiegandii:* **a,** twig x1.5; **b,** node x3. **6.** *A. gaspensis:* **a,** twig x1.5; **b,** node x3. **7.** *A. bartramiana:* **a,** twig x1.5; **b,** node x3. **8.** *A. sanguinea:* **a,** twig x1.5; **b,** node x3. **9.** *A. stolonifera:* **a,** twig x1.5; **b,** node x3.

Plate XXVI. **1.** *Physocarpus opulifolius:* **a,** twig x1.5; **b,** node x7; **c,** older branchlet and fruiting branch x1.5. **2.** *Crataegus sp.:* **a,** twig x1.5; **b,** node x9.5. **3.** *Potentilla tridentata:* **a,** aerial portion of plant x1.5; **b,** vestiges of inflorescence x1.5. **4.** *P. fruticosa:* **a,** twig x1.5; **b,** node x6; **c,** node, persistent petiole base removed x9; **d,** inflorescence x1.5; **e,** fruit x12.

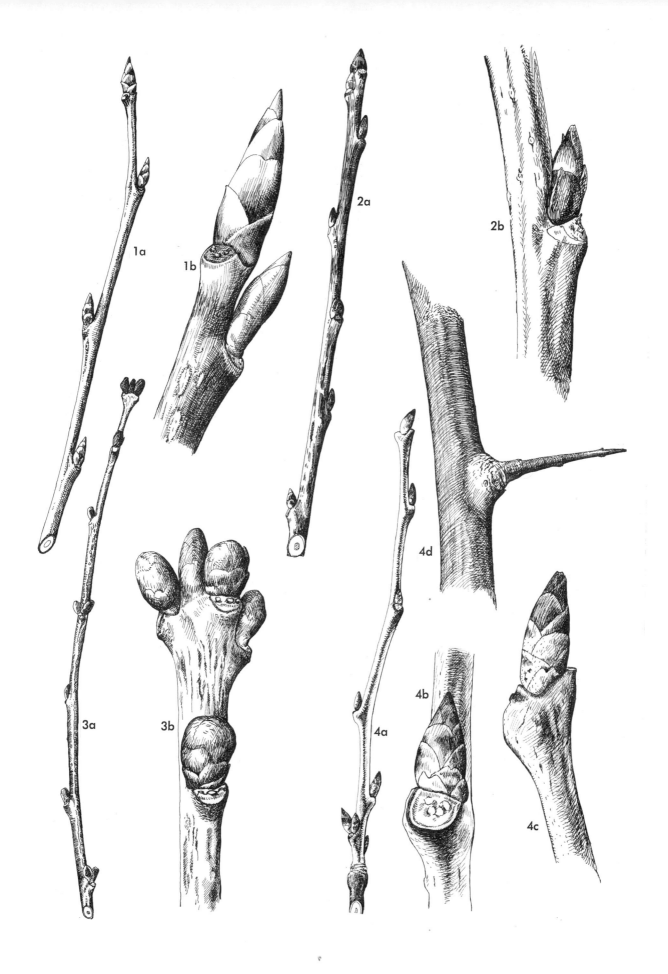

Plate XXVII. **1.** *Prunus virginiana:* **a,** twig x1.5; **b,** tip of twig x6. **2.** *P. serotina:* **a,** twig x1.5; **b,** node x6. **3.** *P. pensylvanica:* **a,** twig x1.5; **b,** tip of twig x6. **4.** *P. nigra:* **a,** twig x1.5; **b,** node x6; **c,** pseudoterminal bud x6; **d,** spinescent branch x1.9.

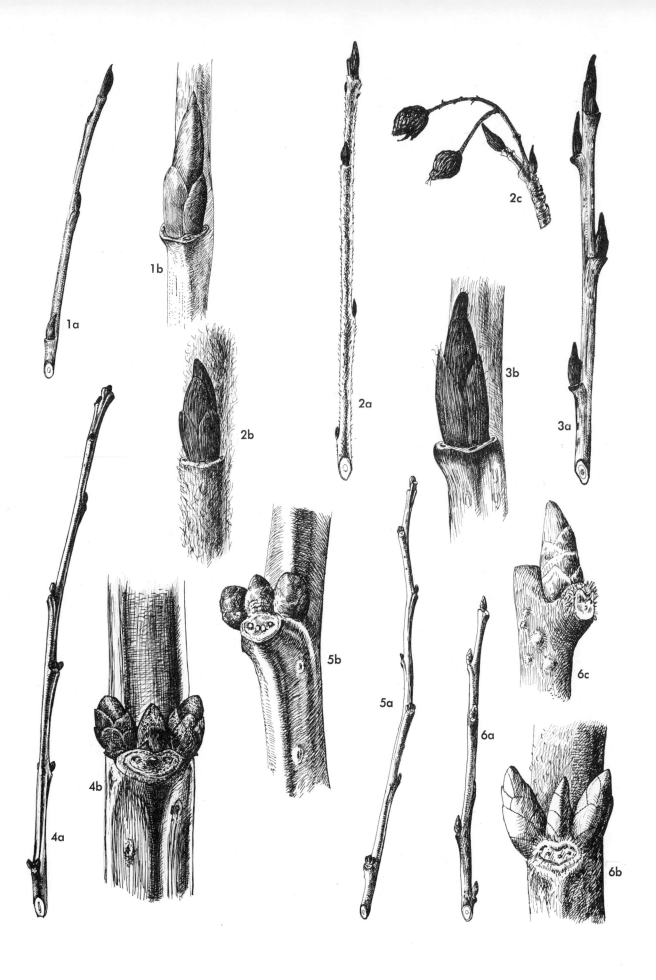

Plate XXVIII. **1.** *Pyrus melanocarpa:* **a,** twig x1.5; **b,** node x7.5. **2.** *P. floribunda:* **a,** twig x1.5; **b,** node x5.5; **c,** fruit x1.5. **3.** *P. aucuparia* X *floribunda:* **a,** twig x1.5; **b,** node x5.5. **4.** *Prunus depressa:* **a,** twig x1.5; **b,** node x9. **5.** *P. susquehanae:* **a,** twig x1.5; **b,** node x9. **6.** *P. maritima:* **a,** twig x1.5; **b,** node x7.5; **c,** pseudotermial bud x9.

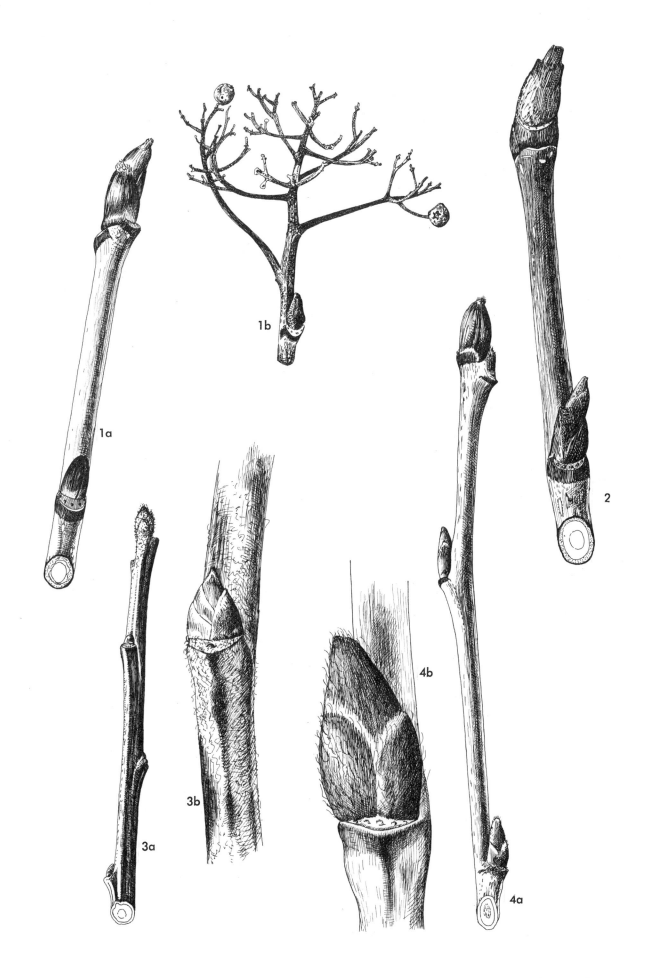

Plate XXIX. **1.** *Pyrus americana;* **a,** twig x1.5; **b,** inflorescence x1.5. **2.** *P. decora:* twig x1.5. **3.** *P. malus:* **a,** twig x1.5; **b,** node x6. **4.** *P. aucuparia:* **a,** twig x1.5; **b,** node x6.

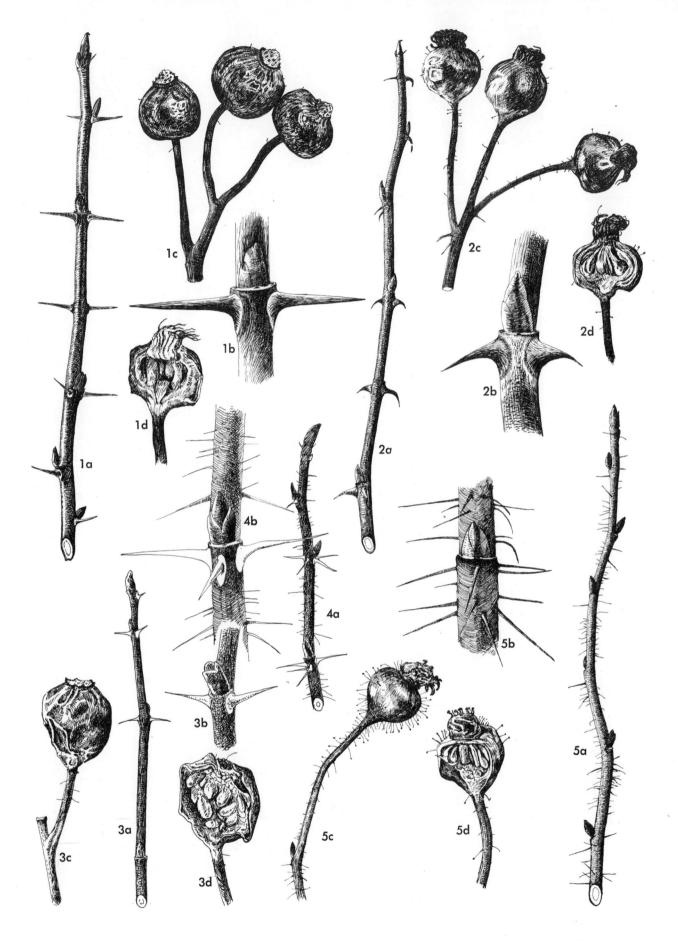

Plate XXX. 1. *Rosa virginiana:* **a**, twig x 1.5; **b**, node x3.7; **c**, fruit x1.5; **d**, cross-section of fruit x1.5. 2. *R. palustris:* **a**, twig x1.5; **b**, node x3.7; **c**, fruit x1.5; **d**, cross-section of fruit x1.5. 3. *R. carolina:* **a**, twig x1.5; **b**, node x3.7; **c**, fruit x1.5; **d**, cross-section of fruit x1.5. 4. *R. acicularis:* **a**, twig x1.5; **b**, node x3.7. 5. *R. nitida:* **a**, twig x1.5; **b**, node x3.7; **c**, fruit x1.5; **d**, cross-section of fruit x1.5.

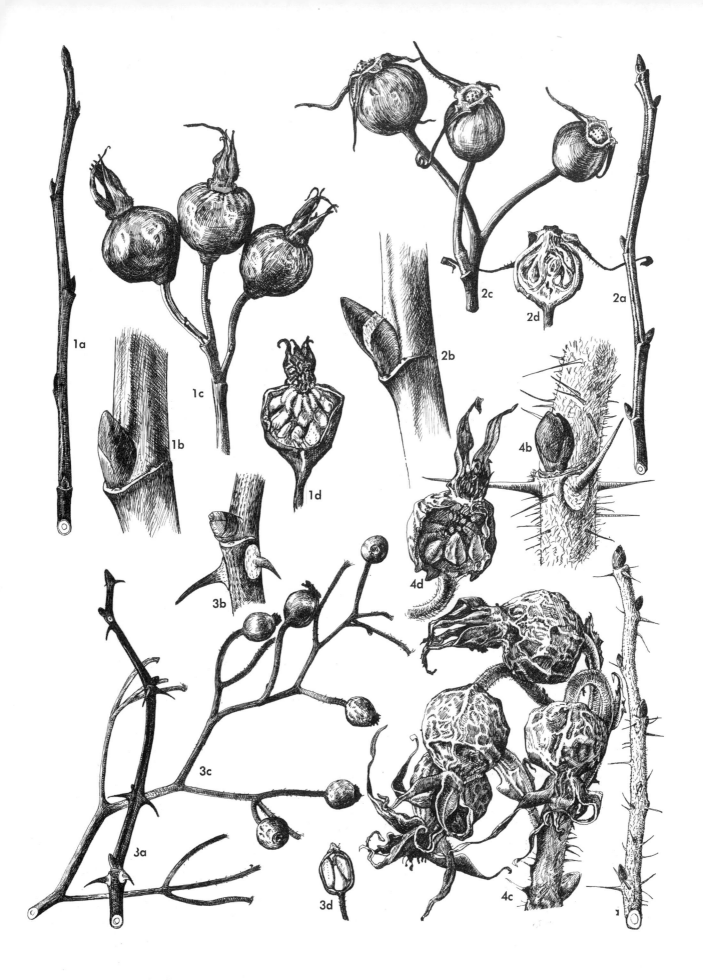

Plate XXXI. **1.** *Rosa blanda:* **a,** twig x1.5; **b,** node x7.5; **c,** fruit x1.5; **d,** cross-section of fruit x1.5. **2.** *R. johannensis:* **a,** twig x1.5; **b,** node x7.5; **c,** fruit x1.5; **d,** cross-section of fruit x1.5. **3.** *R. multiflora:* **a,** twig x1.5; **b,** node x3.7; **c,** fruit x1.5; **d,** cross-section of fruit x1.5. **4.** *R. rugosa:* **a,** twig x1.5; **b,** node x2.3; **c,** fruit x1.5; **d,** cross-section of fruit x1.5.

Plate XXXII. **1.** *Rubus idaeus:* **a,** primocane x1.5; **b,** node x2.3; **c,** inflorescence x¾. **2.** *R. canadensis:* **a,** primocane x1.5; **b,** node x3; **c,** portion of inflorescence x¾; **d,** axis and branch of inflorescence x4.5. **3.** *R. odoratus:* **a,** primocane x1.5; **b,** node x2.3; **c,** portion of inflorescence x¾. **4.** *R. occidentalis:* **a,** primocane x1.5; **b,** node x2.3; **c,** portion of inflorescence x¾. **5.** *R. alleghensiensis:* **a,** primocane x1.5; **b,** node x2.3; **c,** portion of inflorescence x¾; **d,** axis and branches of inflorescence x4.5. **6.** *R. pubescens:* **a,** primocane x1.5; **b,** node x2.3.

Plate XXXIII. 1. *Spiraea tomentosa:* **a,** fruiting twig x¾; **b,** node x4.5; **c,** fruit x15. **2.** *S. latifolia:* **a,** fruiting twig x¾; **b,** node x7; **c,** fruit, top view x15; **d,** same, lateral view x12. **3.** *Sorbaria sorbifolia:* **a,** inflorescence x¾; **b,** fruit x15; **c,** node x2.3. **4.** *Rubus hispidus:* **a,** primocane x¾; **b,** node x3.

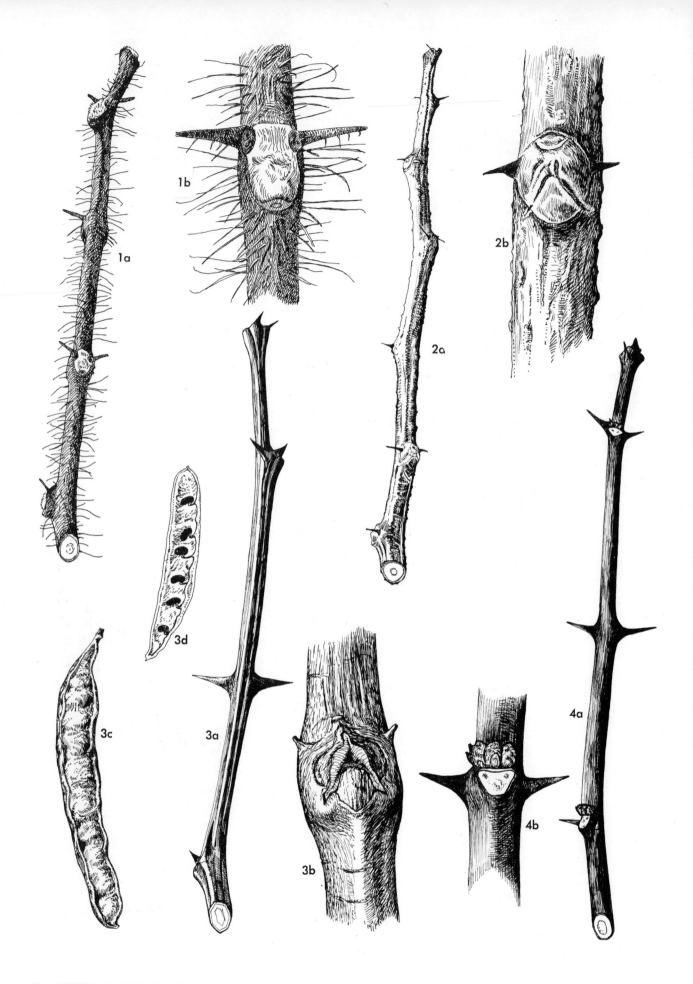

Plate XXXIV. **1.** *Robinia hispida:* **a,** twig x1.5; **b,** node x4.7. **2.** *R. viscosa:* **a,** twig x1.5; **b,** node x4.5. **3.** *R. pseudo-acacia:* **a,** twig x1.5; **b,** node x4.5; **c,** outside of fruit x¾; **d,** inside of fruit x¾;. **4.** *Zanthoxylum americanum:* **a,** twig x1.5; **b,** node x3.

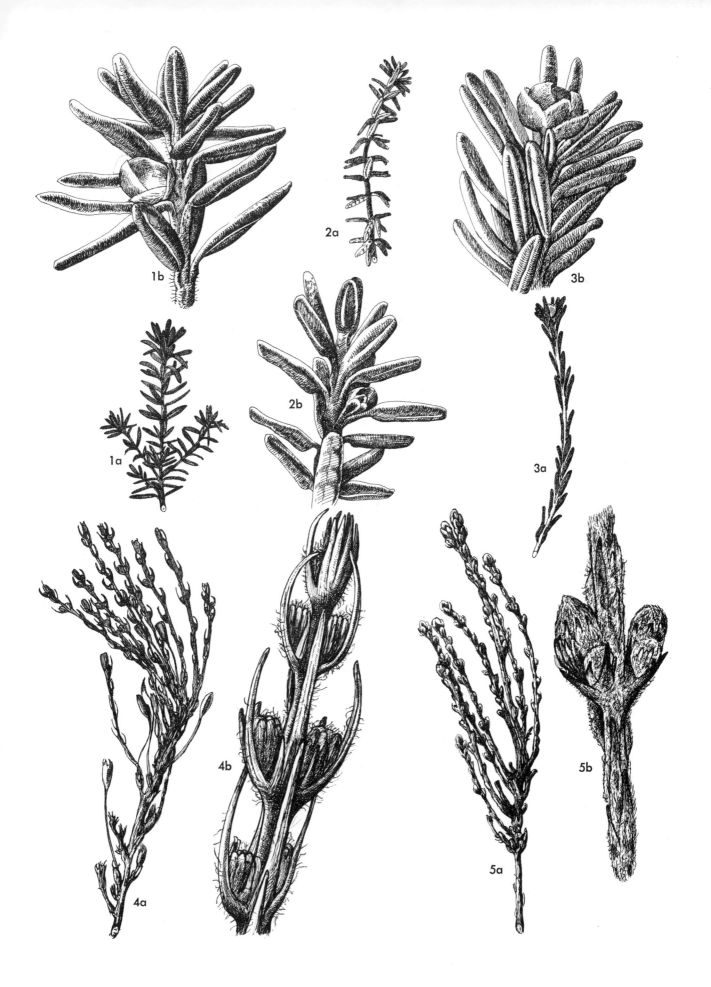

Plate XXXV. **1.** *Empetrum atropurpureum:* **a,** portion of plant x1.5; **b,** tip of twig x8. **2.** *E. nigrum:* **a,** portion of plant x1.5; **b,** tip of twig x6. **3.** *Corema conradii:* **a,** twig x1.5; **b,** tip of twig x8. **4.** *Hudsonia ericoides:* **a,** portion of plant x1.5; **b,** tip of twig x9. **5.** *H. tomentosa:* **a,** portion of plant x1.5; **b,** portion of twig x6.

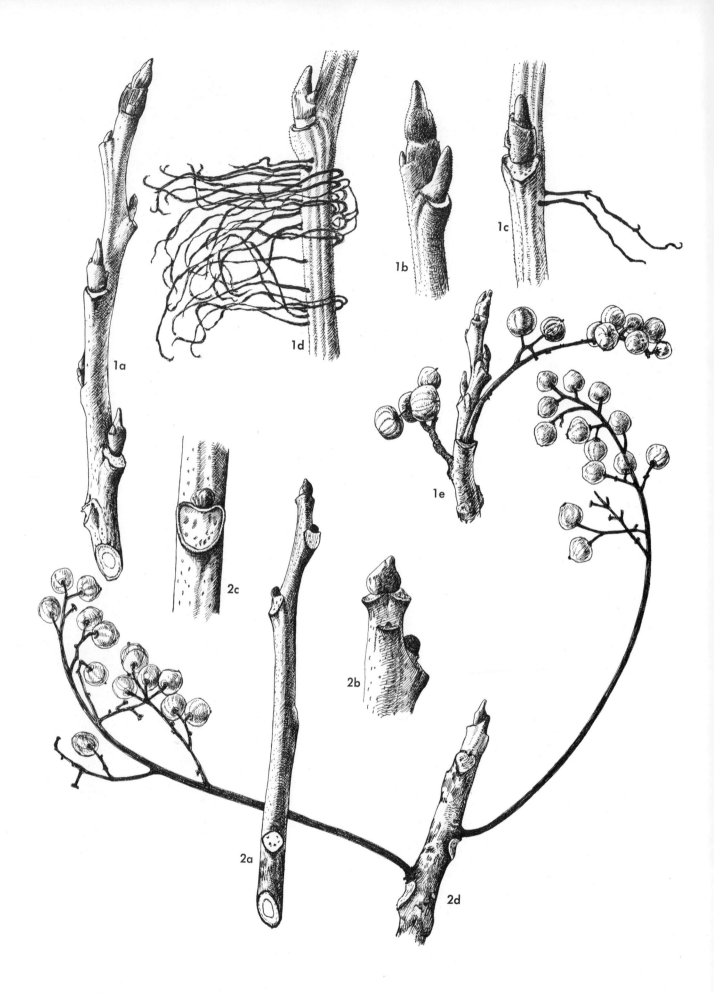

Plate XXXVI. **1.** *Rhus radicans:* **a,** twig x1.5; **b,** tip of twig x3; **c,** node with aerial rootlets, face view x3; **d,** same, lateral view x3; **e,** fruit x1.5. **2.** *R. vernix:* **a,** twig x1.5; **b,** tip of twig x3; **c,** node x3; **d,** fruit x1.5.

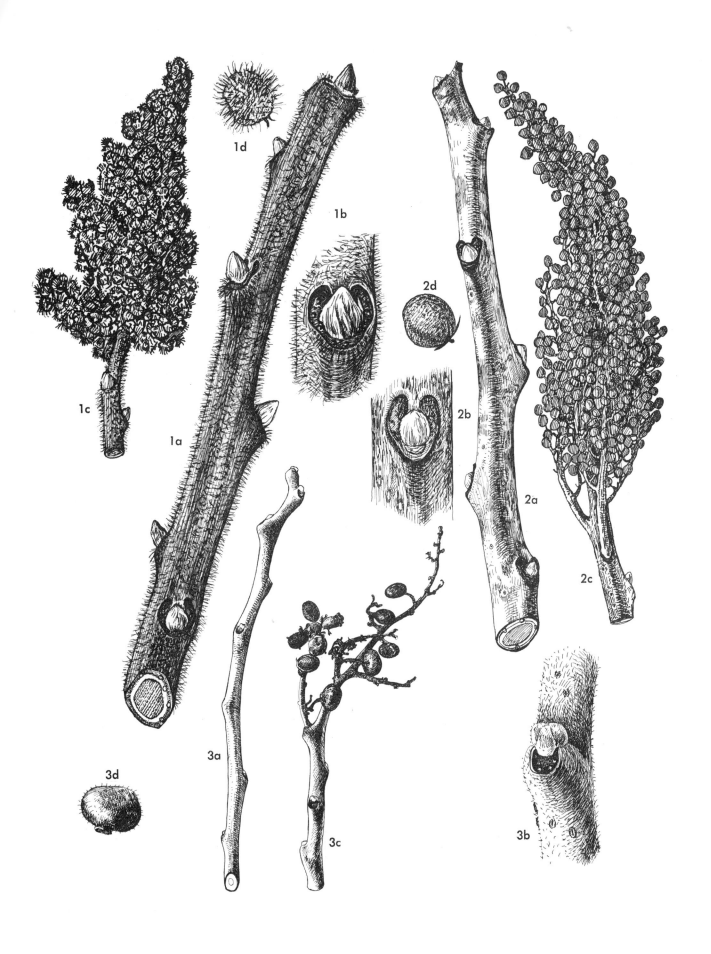

Plate XXXVII. *Rhus typhina:* **a,** twig x1.5; **b,** node x2.3; **c,** inflorescence x¾; **d,** fruit x3. **2.** *R. glabra:* **a,** twig x1.5; **b,** node x2.3; **c,** inflorescence x¾; **d,** fruit x3. **3.** *R. copallina:* **a,** twig x1.5; **b,** node x3.7; **c,** inflorescence x1.5; **d,** fruit x3.

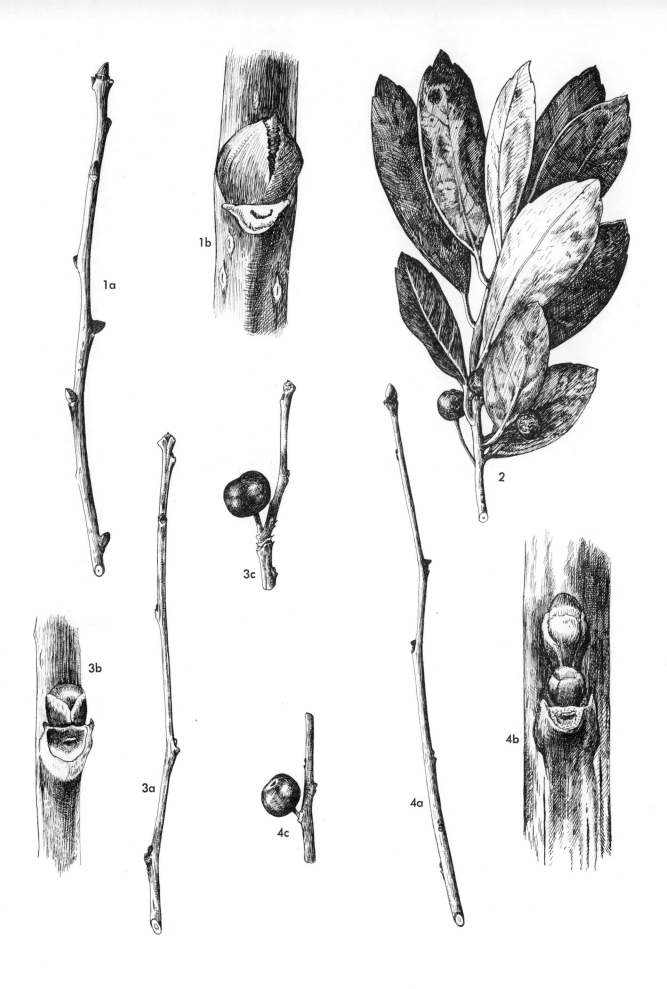

Plate XXXVIII. **1.** *Nemopanthus mucronata:* **a,** twig x1.5; **b,** node x9. **2.** *Ilex glabra:* fruiting twig x1.5. **3.** *I. laevigata:* **a,** twig x1.5; **b,** node x9; **c,** fruiting twig x1.5. **4.** *I. verticillata:* **a,** twig x1.5; **b,** node x9; **c,** fruiting twig x1.5.

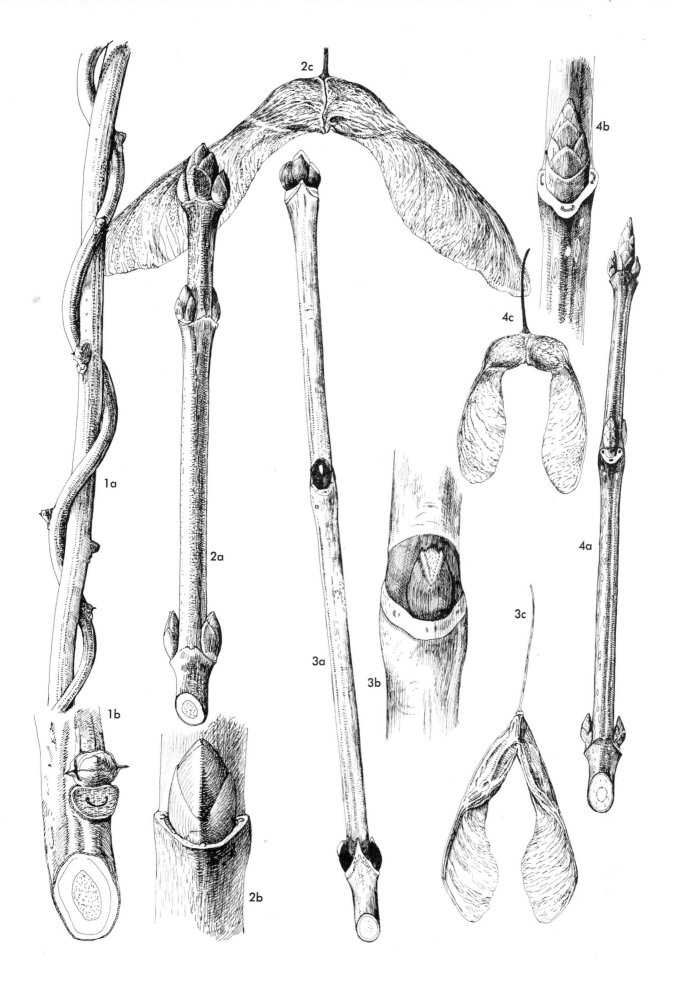

Plate XXXIX. **1.** *Celastrus scandens:* **a,** intertwining twigs x1.5; **b,** node x4.5. **2.** *Acer platanoides:* **a,** twig x1.5; **b,** node x3.7; **c,** fruit x1.5. **3.** *A. negundo:* **a,** twig x1.5; **b,** node x3.7; **c,** fruit x1.5. **4.** *A. saccharum:* **a,** twig x1.5; **b,** node x3.7; **c,** fruit x1.5.

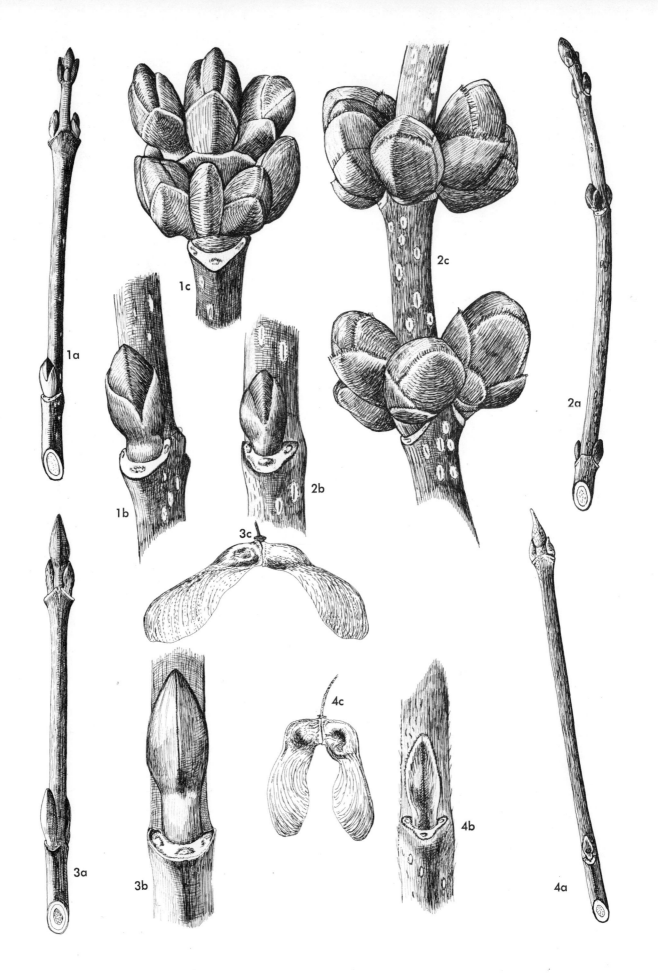

Plate XL. **1.** *Acer rubrum:* **a,** twig x1.5; **b,** node x5.3; **c,** tip of twig with collateral flower buds x5.3. **2.** *A. saccharinum:* **a,** twig x1.5; **b,** node x5.3. **3.** *A. pensylvanicum:* **a,** twig x1.5; **b,** node x3.7; **c,** fruit x1.5. **4.** *A. spicatum:* **a,** twig x1.5; **b,** node x3.7; **c,** fruit x1.5.

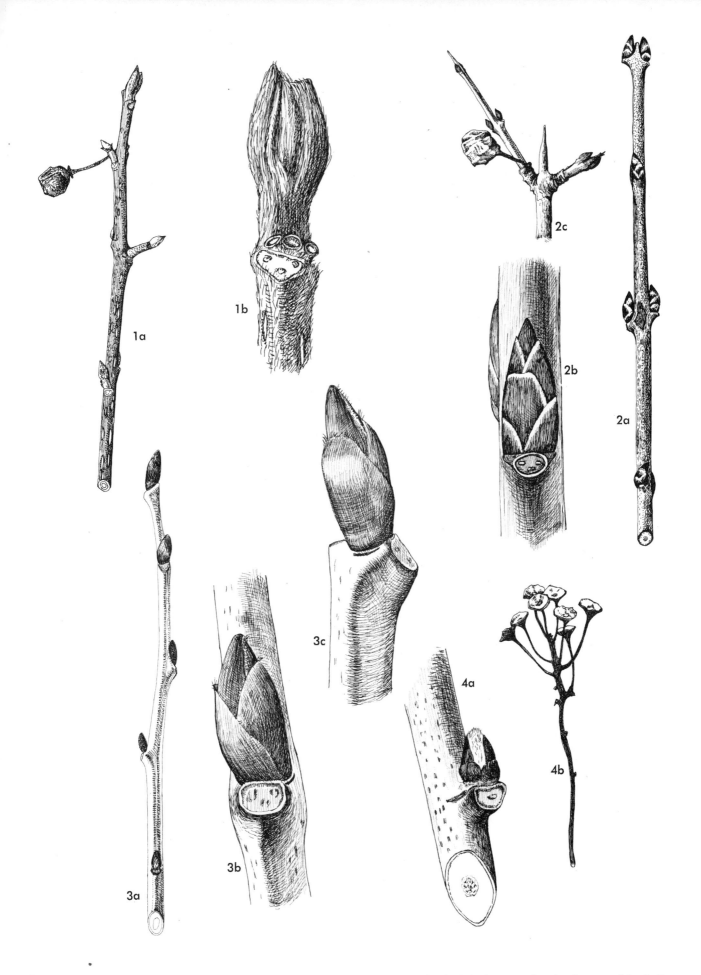

Plate XLI. **1.** *Rhamnus frangula:* **a,** fruiting twig x1.5; **b,** tip of twig showing bud, leaf scar, and peduncle scars x7.5. **2.** *R. cathartica:* **a,** twig x1.5; **b,** node x6; **c,** fruit and spinescent branches x1.5. **3.** *R. alnifolia:* **a,** twig x1.5; **b,** node x7.5; **c,** pseudoterminal bud x7.5. **4.** *Ceanothus americanus:* **a,** node x9; **b,** inflorescence and fruit receptacles x1.5.

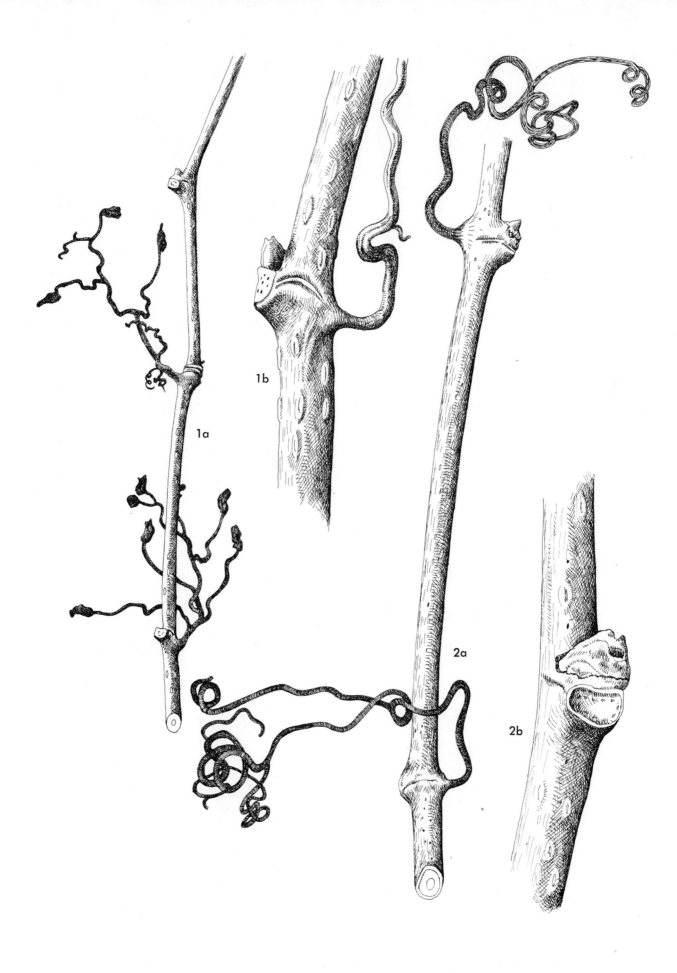

Plate XLII. 1. *Parthenocissus quinquefolia:* **a,** twig x1.5; **b,** node x3. **2.** *Parthenocissus inserta:* **a,** twig x1.5; **b,** node x3.

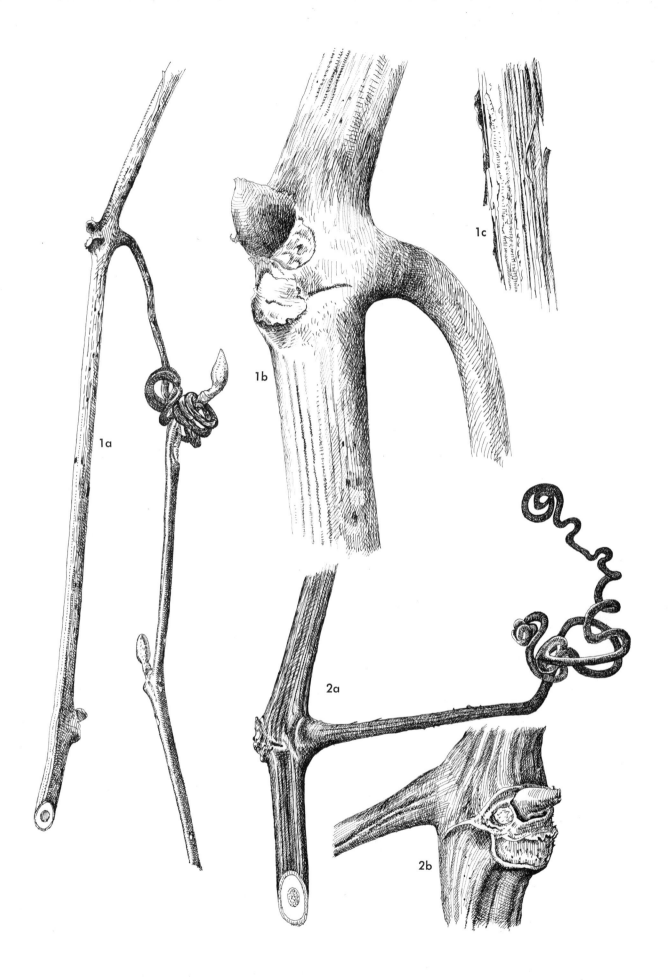

Plate XLIII. **1.** *Vitis riparia:* **a,** twig x1.5; **b,** node x4.5; **c,** portion of second-year branchlet x1.5. **2.** *Vitis labrusca:* **a,** twig x1.5; **b,** node x3.

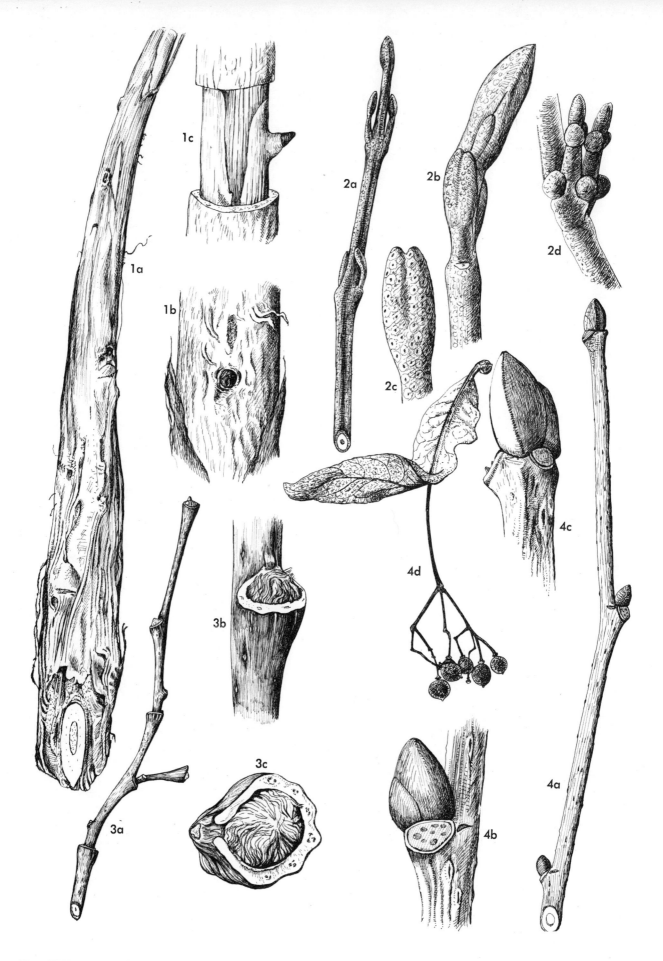

Plate XLIV. **1.** *Decodon verticillatus:* **a,** base of stem x1.5; **b,** node, face view x3; **c,** node (corky layer removed), lateral view x3. **2.** *Shepherdia canadensis:* **a,** twig x1.5; **b,** tip of twig x3.7; **c,** bud x6; **d,** short branchlets with flower buds x4.5. **3.** *Dirca palustris:* **a,** two year's growth x1.5; **b,** node x6; **c,** pseudoterminal bud (top view) x9. **4.** *Tilia americana:* **a,** twig x1.5; **b,** node x4.5; **c,** pseudoterminal bud x4.5; **d,** inflorescence, bract, and fruit x¾.

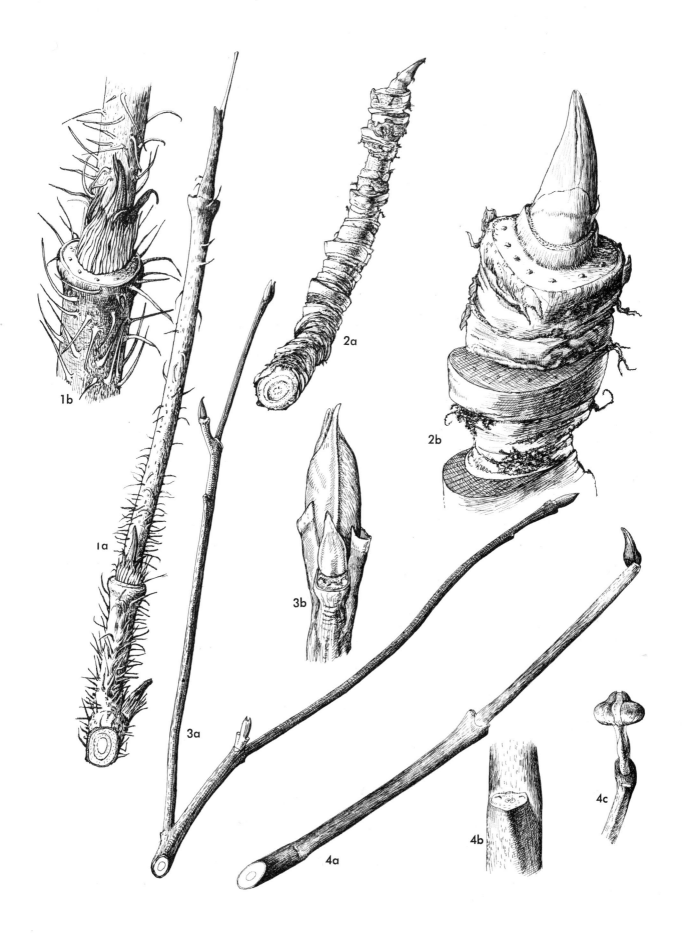

Plate XLV. **1.** *Aralia hispida:* **a,** twig x1.5; **b,** node x3.7. **2.** *A. nudicaulis:* **a,** aerial portion of plant x1.5; **b,** several leaf scars and solitary terminal bud x4.7. **3.** *Cornus alternifolia:* **a,** twig x1.5; **b,** tip of twig x8. **4.** *C. florida:* **a,** twig x1.5; **b,** node x6; **c,** flower bud x1.5.

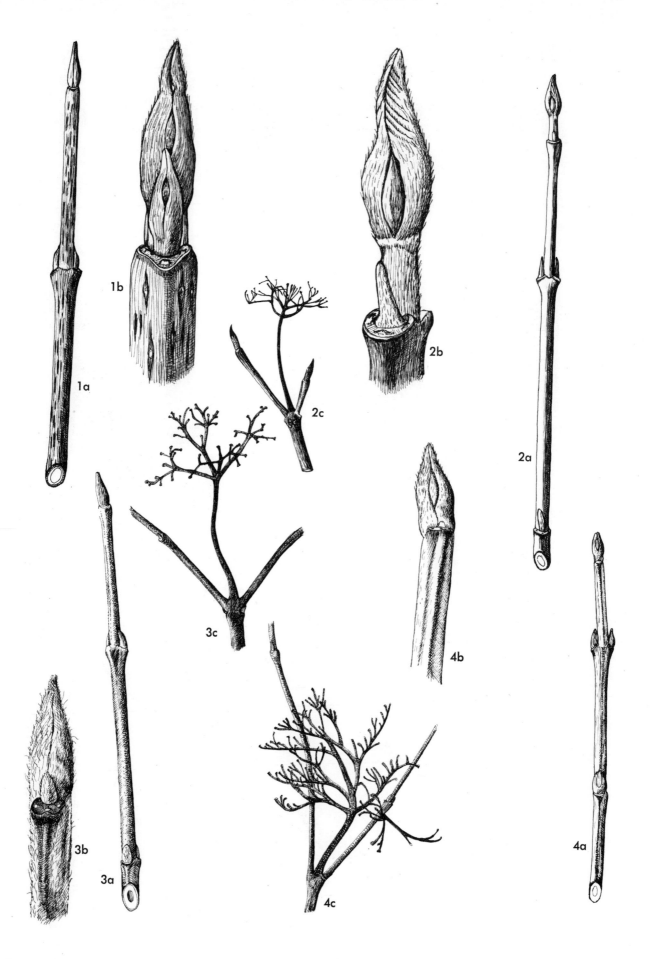

Plate XLVI. **1.** *Cornus rugosa:* **a,** twig x1.5; **b,** tip of twig x4.5. **2.** *C. stolonifera:* **a,** twig x1.5; **b,** tip of twig x6; **c,** inflorescence x¾. **3.** *C. obliqua:* **a,** twig x1.5; **b,** tip of twig x6; **c,** inflorescence x¾. **4.** *C. racemosa:* **a,** twig x1.5; **b,** tip of twig x6; **c,** inflorescence x¾.

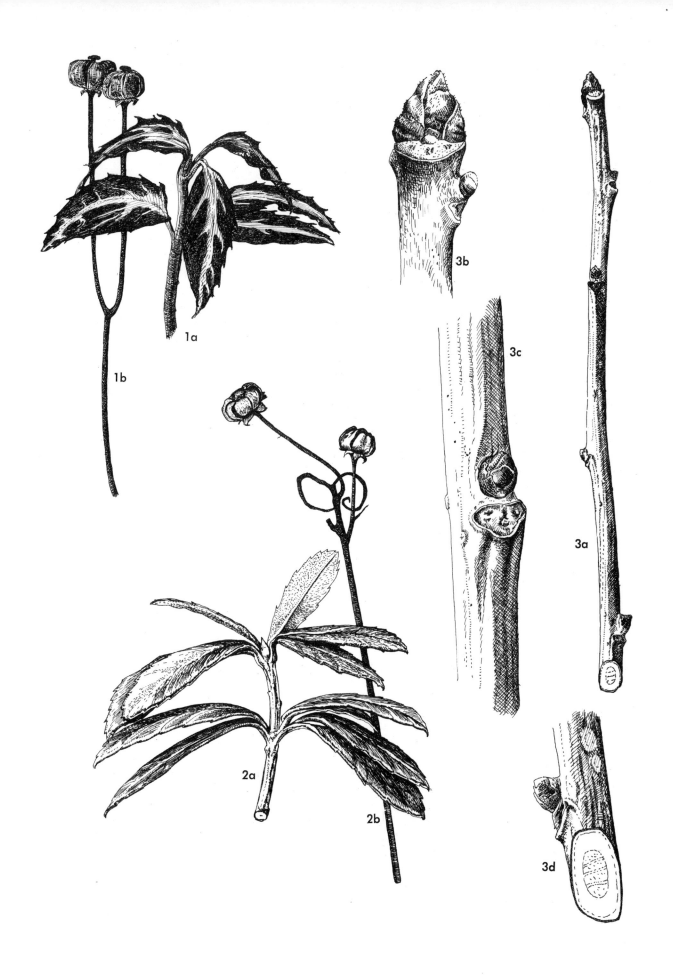

Plate XLVII. **1.** *Chimaphila maculata:* **a,** twig x1.5; **b,** inflorescence x1.5. **2.** *C. umbellata* var. *cisatlantica:* **a,** twig x1.1; **b,** inflorescence x1.9. **3.** *Nyssa sylvatica:* **a,** twig x1.5; **b,** tip of twig x4.5; **c,** node x4.5; **d,** pith x3.

Plate XLVIII. **1.** *Clethra alnifolia:* **a,** twig x2.3; **b,** tip of twig x3.7; **c,** fruiting twig x1.5; **d,** stellate pubescence x40. **2.** *Lyonia ligustrina:* **a,** twig x1.5; **b,** node x7; **c,** pseudoterminal bud x8; **d,** inflorescence x1.5. **3.** *Andromeda glaucophylla:* **a,** fruiting branch x1.5; **b,** fruit x1.5.

Plate XLIX.   **1.** *Rhododendron maximum:*   **a,** fruiting twig x¾;   **b,** flower bud x1.5. **2.** *R. lapponicum:*   **a,** twig x1.5;   **b,** fruit x2.7. **3.** *R. canadense:*   **a,** fruiting twig x1.5;   **b,** tip of twig x5.2. **4.** *R. viscosum:*   **a,** twig x1.5;   **b,** tip of twig x4.5.

Plate L. **1.** *Kalmia polifolia:* **a,** twig x1.9; **b,** inflorescence x1.5; **c,** flower bud and tip of twig x2.3. **2.** *K. angustifolia:* **a,** fruiting twig x1.5; **b,** tip of twig x1.5; **c,** fruit x3. **3.** *K. latifolia:* **a,** twig x ¾; **b,** fruit x¾.

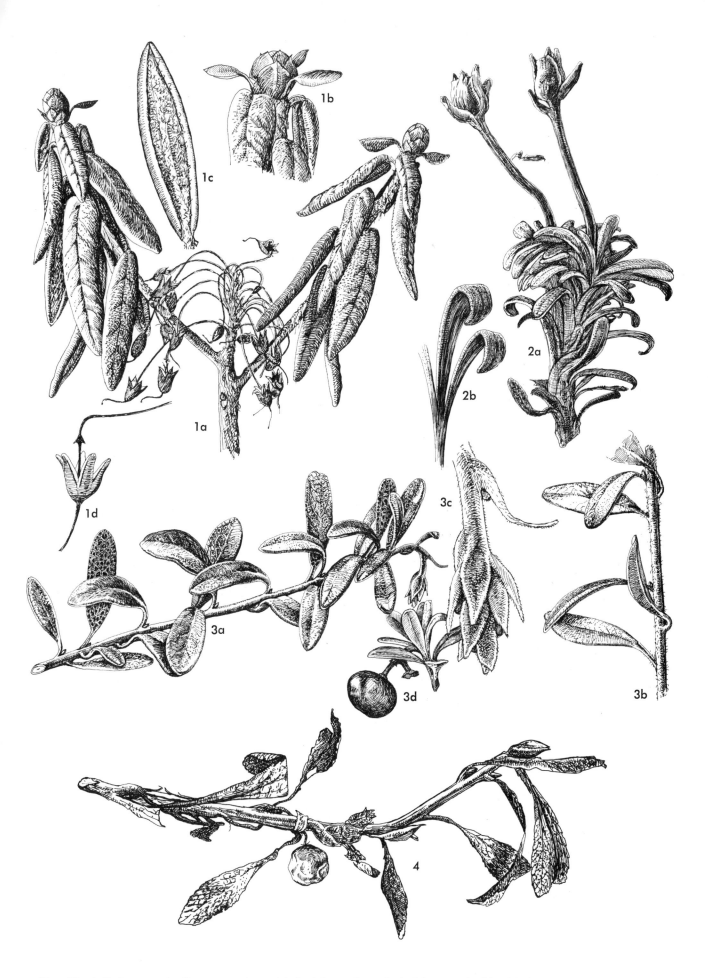

Plate LI. **1.** *Ledum groenlandicum:* **a,** twigs and fruit x1.5; **b,** flower bud x2.3; **c,** underside of leaf x1.5; **d,** capsule x4.5. **2.** *Diapensia lapponica:* **a,** fruiting stems x2.5; **b,** leaves x6. **3.** *Arctostaphylos uva-ursi* var. *coactilis:* **a,** twig x1.5; **b,** same x1.5; **c,** bud cluster x6; **d,** fruiting twig x1.5. **4.** *A. alpina:* fruiting twig x2.

Plate LII. **1.** *Loiseleuria procumbens:* **a,** twig x3; **b,** tip of twig x5; **c,** underside of leaf x6. **2.** *Cassiope hypnoides:* **a,** fertile stem x3; **b,** capsule and peduncle x8. **3.** *Calluna vulgaris:* **a,** fertile stem x2; **b,** several nodes x8. **4.** *Phyllodoce caerulea:* **a,** tip of stem x2; **b,** underside of leaf x7.

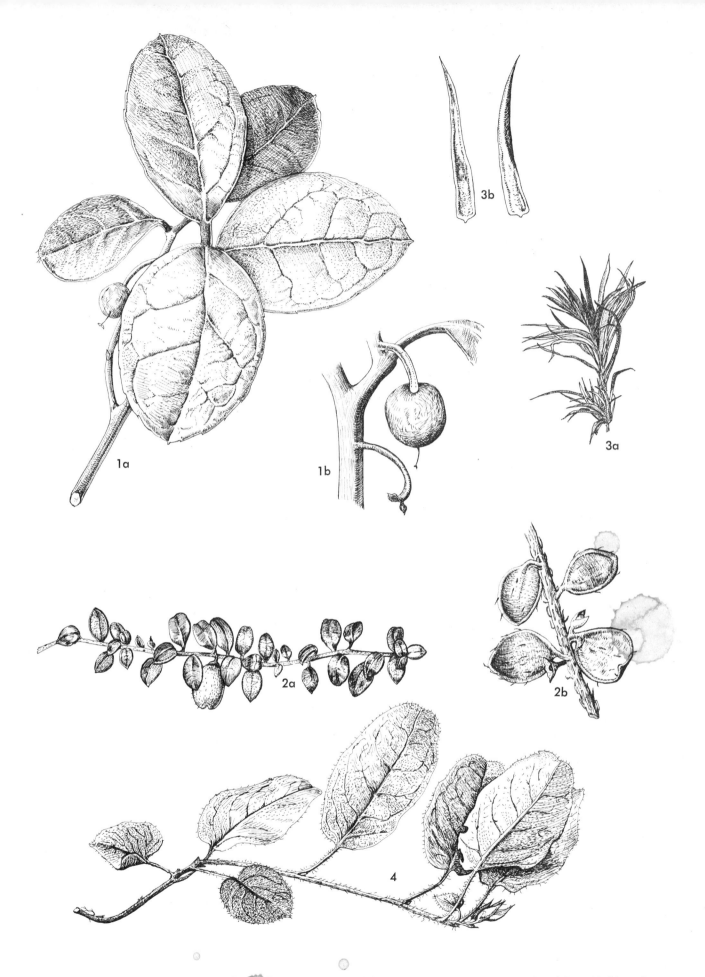

Plate LIII. **1.** *Gaultheria procumbens:* **a,** aerial portion of plant x1.5; **b,** fruit and peduncle x3. **2.** *G. hispidula:* **a,** fruiting twig x1.5; **b,** underside of twig and leaves showing empty calyces x3.7. **3.** *Phlox subulata:* **a,** tip of shoot x1.5; **b,** leaves x2.3. **4.** *Epigaea repens* var. *glabrifolia:* stem and leaves x¾.

Plate LIV. **1.** *Vaccinium vitis-idaea* var. *minus:* **a,** twig x1.5; **b,** underside of leaf x2.3; **c,** tip of fruiting branch x1.5; **d,** fruit, top view x1.5. **2.** *V. macrocarpon:* **a,** portion of stem and fruiting twig x1.5; **b,** tip of twig x3; **c,** fruit (top view) x1.5. **3.** *V. oxycoccos:* **a,** portion of stem and fruiting twig x1.5; **b,** tip of twig x3; **c,** fruit (top view) x1.5. **4.** *Chamaedaphne calyculata* var. *angustifolia:* **a,** twig x1.5; **b,** tip of twig with flower buds x6; **c,** inflorescence x1.7.

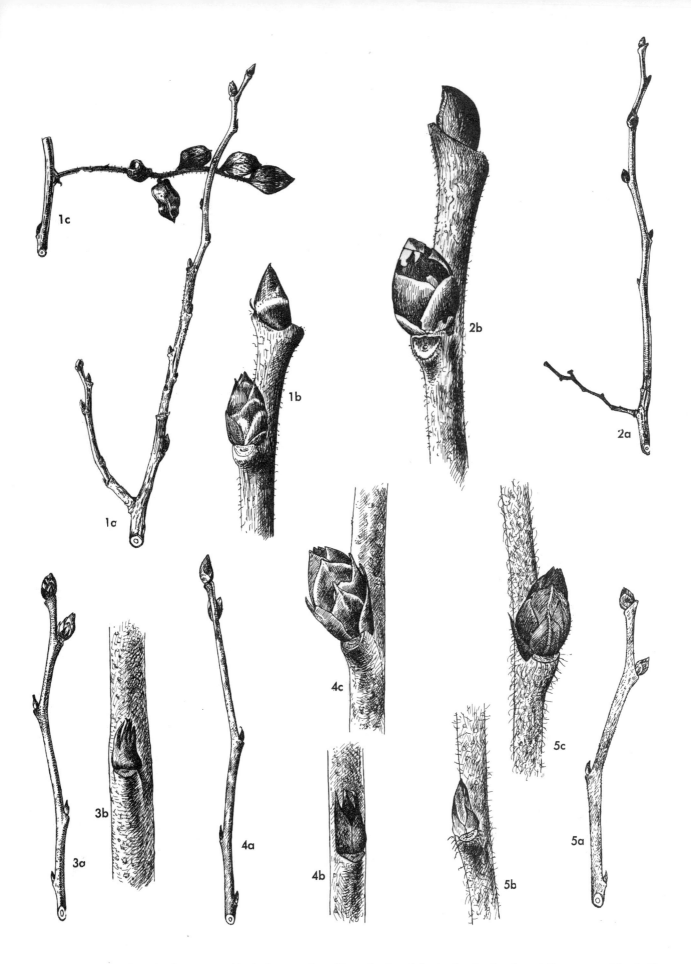

Plate LV. **1.** *Gaylussacia dumosa* var. *bigeloviana:* **a,** branchlet and twigs x1.5; **b,** tip of twig x6; **c,** inflorescence x1.5. **2.** *G. baccata:* **a,** twig and inflorescence x1.5; **b,** tip of twig x8. **3.** *Vaccinium caesariense:* **a,** twig x1.5; **b,** node x6. **4.** *V. corymbosum:* **a,** twig x1.5; **b,** node with vegetative bud x6; **c,** node with flower bud x6. **5.** *V. atrococcum:* **a,** twig x1.5; **b,** node with vegetative bud x6; **c,** node with flower bud x6.

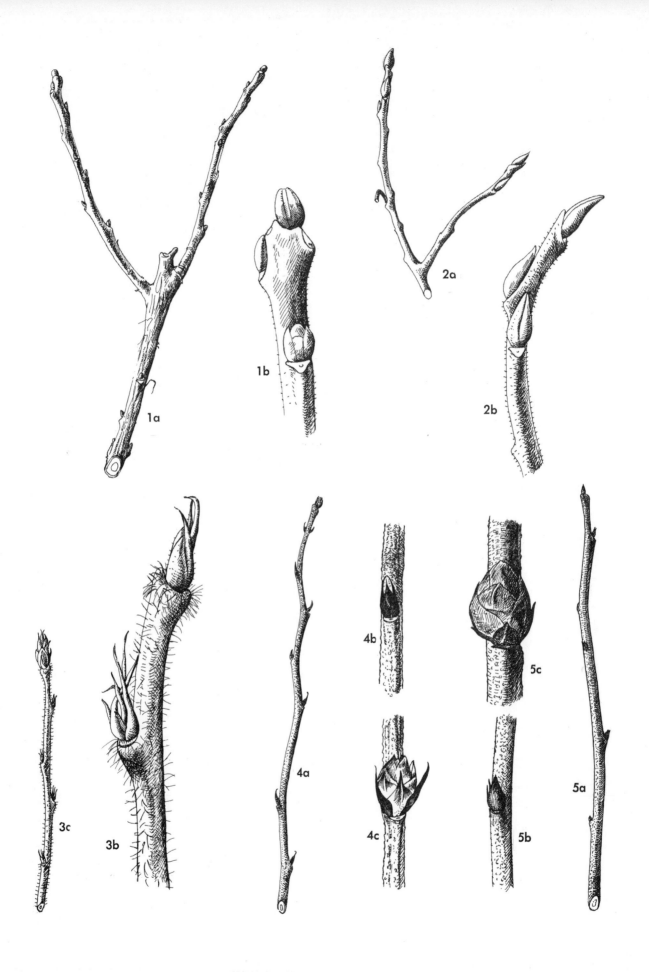

Plate LVI. **1.** *Vaccinium uliginosum* var. *alpinum:* **a,** branchlet and twigs x1.5; **b,** tip of twig x4.5. **2.** *V. cespitosum:* **a,** twig x1.5; **b,** tip of twig x4.5. **3.** *V. myrtilloides:* **a,** twig x1.5; **b,** tip of twig x6. **4.** *V. angustifolium* var. *laevifolium:* **a,** twig x1.5; **b,** vegetative bud x4.5; **c,** flower bud x4.5. **5.** *V. vacillans:* **a,** twig x1.5; **b,** vegetative bud x4.5; **c,** flower bud x4.5.

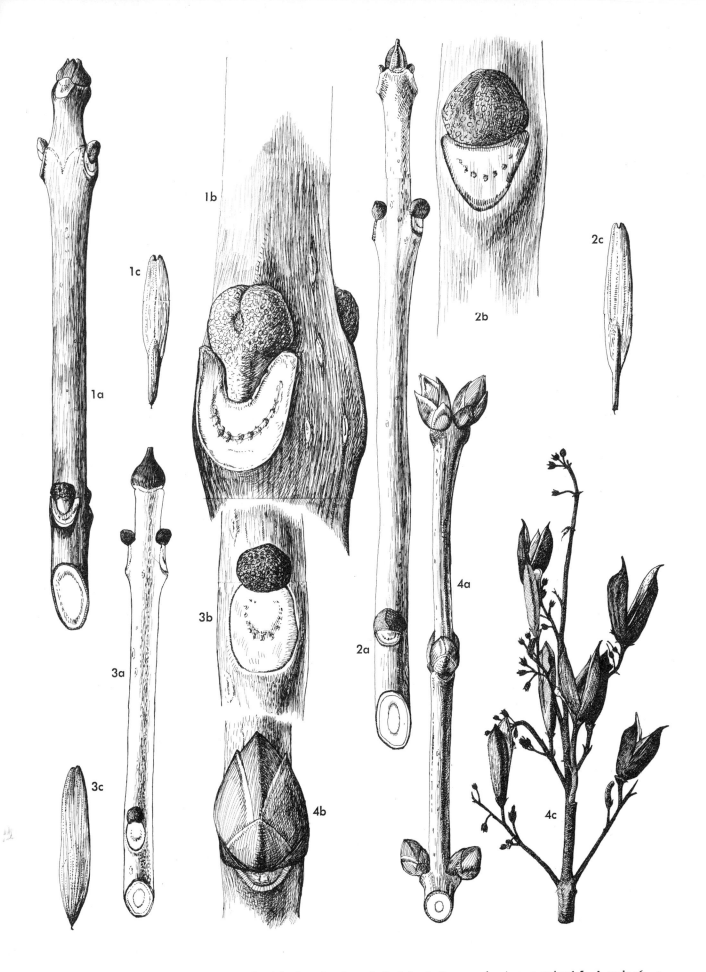

Plate LVII. **1.** *Fraxinus americana:* **a,** twig x1.5; **b,** node x6; **c,** fruit x1.1. **2.** *F. pennsylvanica:* **a,** twig x1.5; **b,** node x6; **c,** fruit x1.1. **3.** *F. nigra:* **a,** twig x1.5; **b,** node x4.5; **c,** fruit x1.1. **4.** *Syringa vulgaris:* **a,** twig x1.5; **b,** node x4.5; **c,** inflorescence x1.5.

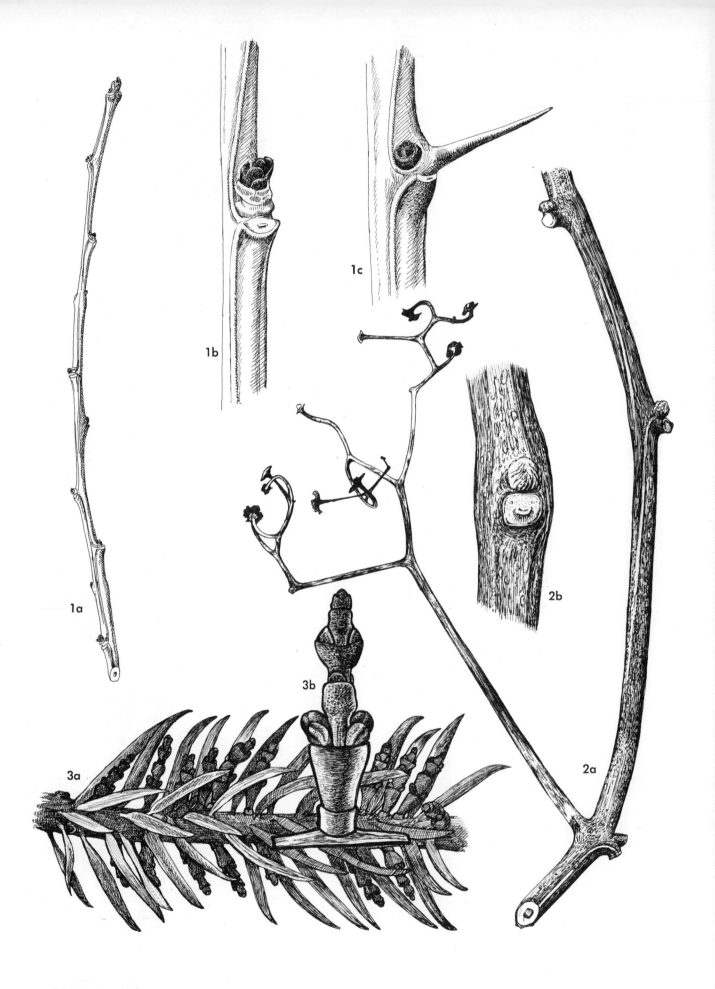

Plate LVIII. **1.** *Lycium chinense:* **a,** twig x1.5; **b,** node x7.5; **c,** node and spine x7.5. **2.** *Solanum dulcamara:* **a,** twig and inflorescence x1.5; **b,** node x4.5. **3.** *Arceuthobium pusillum:* **a,** many plants parasitizing *Picea mariana* x3; **b,** plant x7.5.

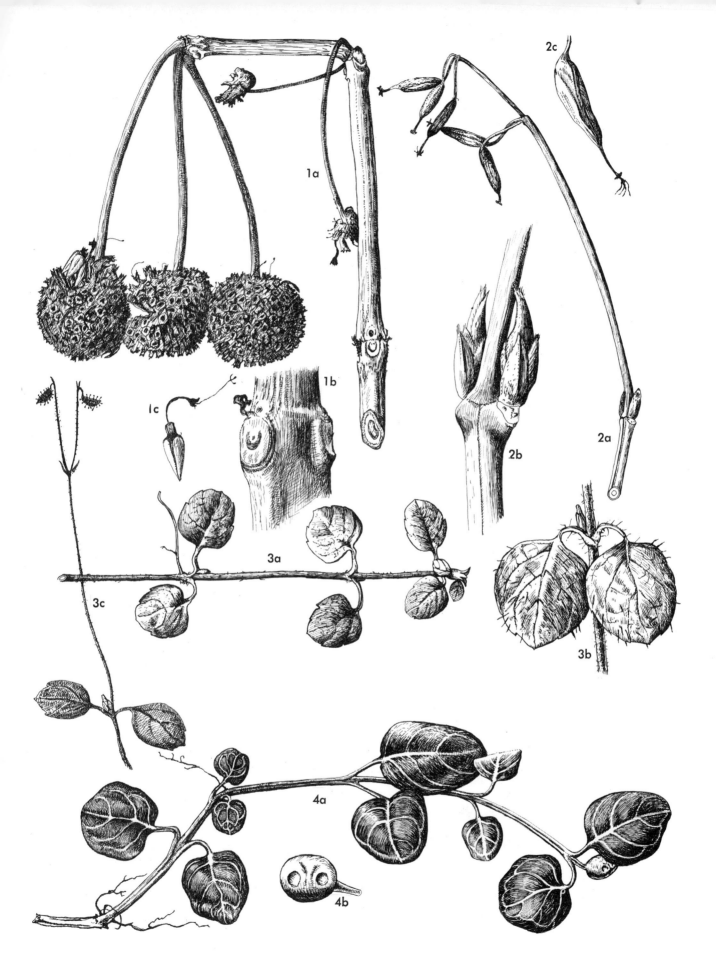

Plate LIX. **1.** *Cephalanthus occidentalis:* **a,** fruiting twig x1.5; **b,** node x3.7; **c,** fruit x2.3. **2.** *Diervilla lonicera:* **a,** fruiting twig x1.5; **b,** node x4.5; **c,** fruit x3. **3.** *Linnaea borealis* var. *americana:* **a,** twig x1.5; **b,** node x3; **c,** fruiting twig x1.5. **4.** *Mitchella repens:* **a,** twig x1.5; **b,** fruit (top view) x2.3.

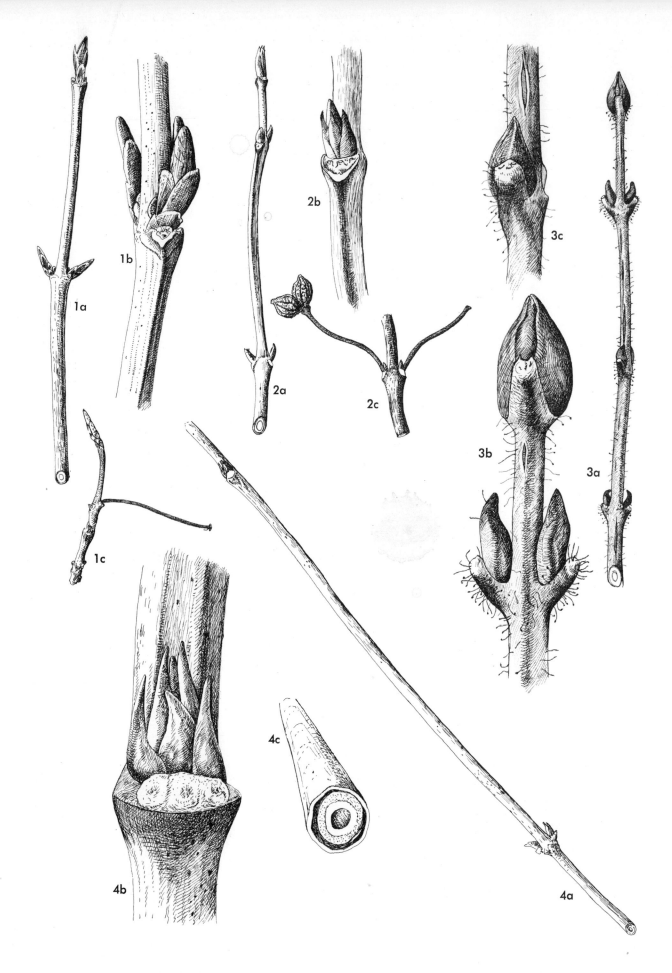

Plate LX. **1.** *Lonicera canadensis:* **a,** twig x1.5; **b,** node x4.7; **c,** fruiting twig with peduncle x1.5. **2.** *L. oblongifolia:* **a,** twig x1.5; **b,** node x4.7; **c,** fruiting twig x1.5. **3.** *L. villosa:* **a,** twig x1.5; **b,** tip of twig x4.7; **c,** node x4.7. **4.** *L. dioica:* **a,** twig x1.5; **b,** node x12; **c,** hollow pith.

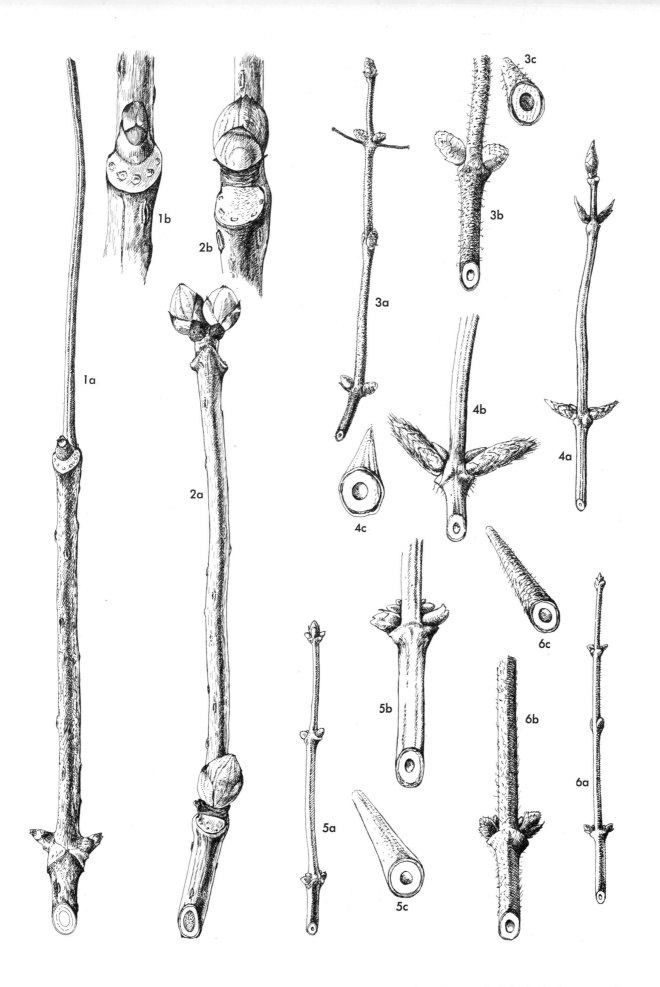

Plate LXI. **1.** *Sambucus canadensis:* **a,** twig x1.5; **b,** node x3. **2.** *S. pubens:* **a,** twig x1.5; **b,** node x2.3. **3.** *Lonicera morrowi:* **a,** twig with 2 peduncles x1.5; **b,** node x3; **c,** hollow pith. **4.** *L. xylosteum:* **a,** twig x1.5; **b,** node x3; **c,** hollow pith. **5.** *L. tatarica:* **a,** twig x1.5; **b,** node x3; **c,** hollow pith. **6.** X *L. bella:* **a,** twig x1.5; **b,** node x3; **c,** hollow pith.

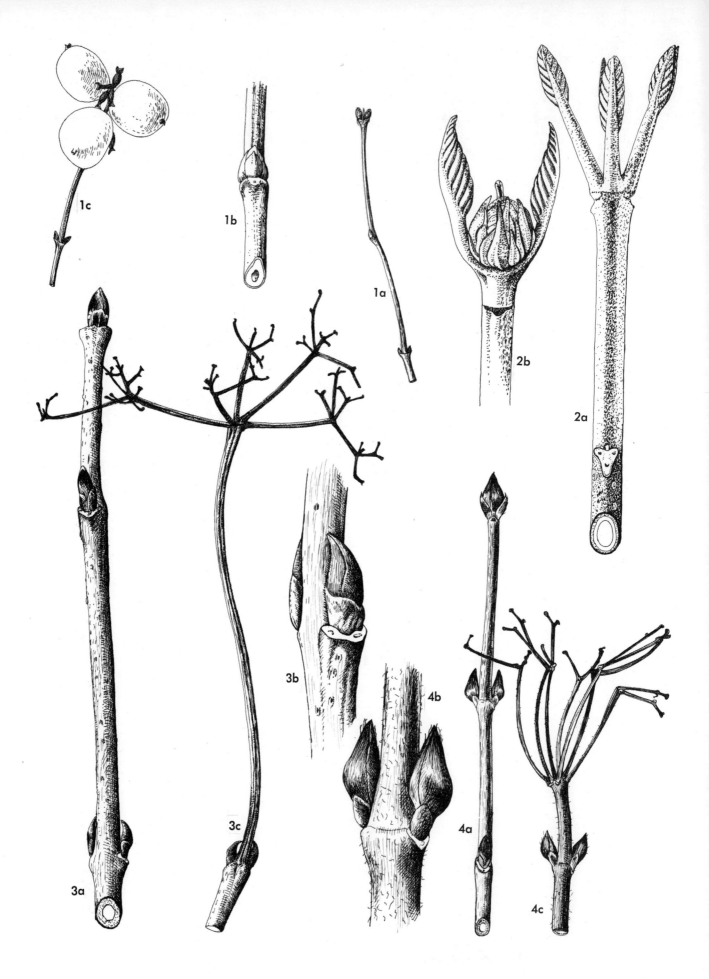

Plate LXII. 1. *Symphoricarpos albus* var. *laevigatus:* **a,** twig x1.5; **b,** node x3.7; **c,** fruiting twig x1.5. **2.** *Viburnum alnifolium:* **a,** twig x1.5; **b,** flower bud x1.5. **3.** *V. recognitum:* **a,** twig x1.5; **b,** node x3.7; **c,** inflorescence x1.5. **4.** *V. acerifolium:* **a,** twig x1.5; **b,** node x3.7; **c,** inflorescence x1.5.

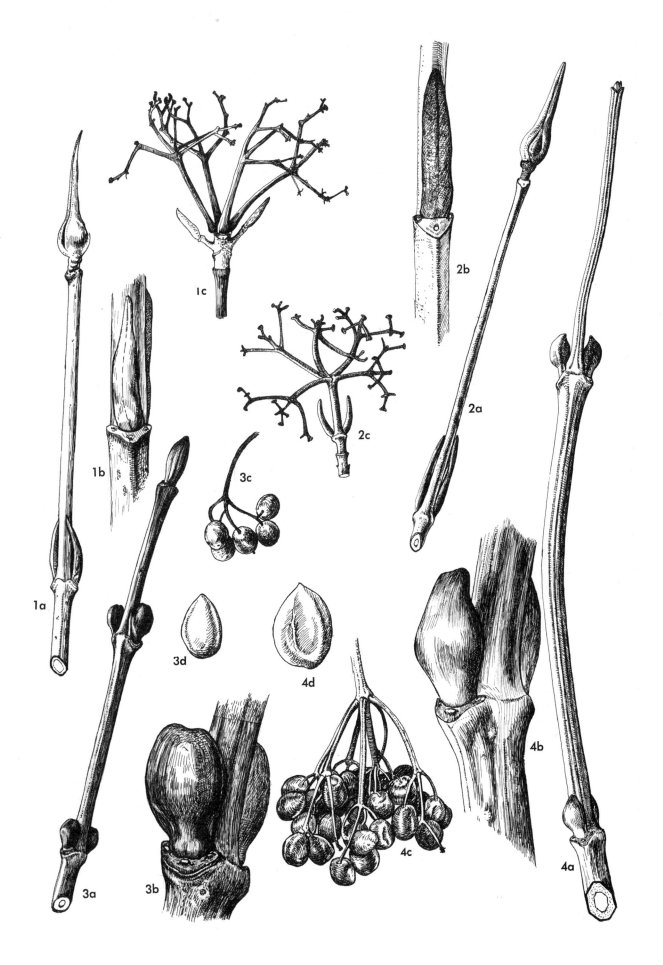

Plate LXIII. 1. *Viburnum lentago:* **a,** twig x1.5; **b,** node x3; **c,** inflorescence x¾. **2.** *V. cassinoides:* **a,** twig x1.5; **b,** node x3.7; **c,** inflorescence x¾. **3.** *V. edule:* **a,** twig x1.5; **b,** node x4.5; **c,** inflorescence x¾; **d,** stone of drupe x2.3. **4.** *V. trilobum:* **a,** twig x1.5; **b,** node x4.5; **c,** inflorescence x¾; **d,** stone of drupe x2.3.